BC Science CONNECTIONS 9
Student Workbook

Development Team

Lionel Sandner
Senior Program Consultant
Victoria, BC

Van Chau
Delview Secondary School
Delta School District #37

Christine Weber
Chilliwack, BC

Michelle Anderson
Columbus, OH

Paul Britton
Curriculum Coordinator (4–9)
Vernon School District #22

Albert Chang
Crofton House School
Vancouver School Board

Gregory Jennens
Brookswood Secondary School
Langley School District #35

Olivia Mak
Vancouver Technical Secondary School
Vancouver School Board

Brian Heimbecker
Orangeville, ON

NELSON

NELSON

For more information contact Nelson Education Ltd., 1120 Birchmount Road, Toronto, Ontario M1K 5G4. Or you can visit our website at nelson.com.

BC Science Connections 9 Student Workbook

The information and activities in this textbook have been carefully developed and reviewed by professionals to ensure safety and accuracy. However, the publisher shall not be liable for any damages resulting, in whole or in part, from the reader's use of the material. Although appropriate safety procedures are discussed and highlighted throughout the textbook, the safety of students remains the responsibility of the classroom teacher, the principal, and the regional school board.

ISBN-13: 978-1-25-965139-7
ISBN-10: 1-25-965139-8

12 13 14   24 23 22

Printed and bound in Canada

DIRECTOR LEARNING SOLUTIONS & PRODUCT DEVELOPMENT (K-12): Lenore Brooks
PUBLISHER: Jean Ford
SENIOR CONTENT MANAGER: Jonathan Bocknek
DEVELOPMENTAL EDITOR: Christine Arnold
SUPERVISING EDITOR: Shannon Martin
COPY EDITOR: Kelli Howey
EDITORIAL ASSISTANT: Erin Hartley
PRODUCTION COORDINATOR: Sarah Strynatka
INTERIOR DESIGN: Brian Lehen Graphic Design Ltd.
COVER DESIGN: Vince Satira
ELECTRONIC PAGE MAKE-UP: Brian Lehen Graphic Design Ltd.

COVER IMAGES: Background: Andrii Vodolazhskyi/Shutterstock; Band Images: left, Masterfile RF; Chris Cheadle/All Canada Photos; goodluz/Shutterstock; Jason Doiy/iStock; Masterfile RF; PhotoSky/Shutterstock

Contents

Safety Symbols Study Notes

Use with textbook page xiv.

Safety symbols appear throughout the textbook with investigations and activities. Refer to the table on page xiv in the textbook. Change each boldfaced heading associated with a symbol into a question. Then, list the potential danger associated with that symbol to answer the question.

1. Question: _____

_____

2. Question: _____

_____

3. Question: _____

_____

4. Question: _____

_____

5. Question: _____

_____

6. Question: _____

_____

7. Question: _____

_____

8. Question: _____

_____

9. Question: _____

_____

10. Question: _____

_____

Safety Symbols

Use with textbook page xiv.

For each description of a procedure in an investigation, identify at least two safety symbols you would expect to see as a reminder of some safety precautions that should be taken.

	Description of Procedure	Safety Symbols	Reason Why These Safety Symbols Are Used
1.	Use a razor blade to cut open a sea star.		
2.	Mix hydrochloric acid with some sodium hydroxide in a test tube.		
3.	Heat a test tube containing calcium carbonate over a Bunsen burner for 5 minutes.		
4.	Add hydrochloric acid to a piece of magnesium ribbon in a test tube. A gas will be produced.		
5.	Prepare a wet mount slide. Then, use a microscope to view plant cells on the slide.		

WHMIS Symbols

Use with textbook page xv.

1. Label the following WHMIS 2015 symbols by placing the name for the symbol inside the box.

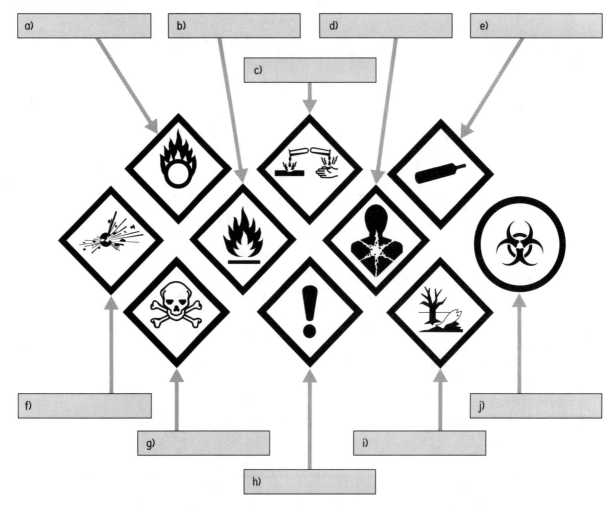

a)

b)

c)

d)

e)

f)

g)

h)

i)

j)

2. Pictograms are used for the WHMIS symbols. What do they convey?

_____

_____

_____

3. Ammonia is commonly found in many laboratories. Below are three WHMIS symbols that are found on the safety label for ammonia.

a) What are the hazards associated with these WHMIS symbols?

_____

_____

_____

b) Describe two safety precautions you should take when using ammonia.

_____

_____

c) Suggest a place to store ammonia.

_____

4. You have been told that a chemical can cause damage to some of your internal organs if there is prolonged exposure to the skin. Also that it should be kept away from heat sources because it is highly flammable.

a) What two WHMIS symbols would be on a safety label for this chemical?

_____

_____

_____

b) What are the hazards associated with these WHMIS symbols?

_____

_____

c) Describe two safety precautions you should take when using this chemical.

_____

_____

The Meaning Behind WHMIS Symbols

Use with textbook page xv.

Match each description on the left with the best WHMIS pictogram on the right.
Each WHMIS pictogram may be used more than once.

Description	WHMIS Pictogram
1. _____ fire hazards	A.
2. _____ is highly reactive	
3. _____ oxidizing hazards	B.
4. _____ explosion hazards	
5. _____ may eat away at metals	C.
6. _____ harmful to eyes and skin	
7. _____ catches fire spontaneously	D.
8. _____ harmful to the environment	
9. _____ compressed gas under pressure	E.
10. _____ may cause serious health effects	
11. _____ has negative impact on aquatic life	F.
12. _____ may cause cancer and birth defects	
13. _____ may cause fire by promoting combustion	G.
14. _____ may explode if container is heated or punctured	
15. _____ may cause damage to organs or allergic reactions	H.
16. _____ may cause explosion due to reactivity, fire, or heat	
17. _____ causes severe skin burns and serious damage to eyes	I.
18. _____ may cause death or toxicity with exposure to small amounts	

19. Identify the four WHMIS symbols that are associated with health hazards. Draw them.

_____

_____

_____

_____

20. Identify the four WHMIS symbols that are associated with physical hazards. Draw them.

_____

_____

_____

_____

21. Identify the WHMIS symbol that is associated with environmental hazards. Draw it.

_____

Safety in the Science Class

Use with textbook pages xvi–xvi and 91–93.

Identify the problem in each scenario shown below. Describe how to fix the problem.

	Scenario	Describe the problem	Describe how to fix the problem
1.			
2.			
3.			
4.			
5.			
6.			

Safety First

Use with textbook pages xvi–xvii and 91–93.

For each scenario, describe what you would do to carry out safe practice in the science classroom.

1. You have read over the procedures to the investigation, but are still unsure about what to do.

   _____

2. You did not have a chance to finish your lunch because you were playing basketball with your friends. You plan to eat your sandwich and drink your juice during your lab.

   _____

3. You are wearing a scarf around your neck and a blouse with loose and baggy sleeves. You are about to turn on the Bunsen burner.

   _____

4. You wash your hands before starting your lab. You reach for the electrical cord to plug it in.

   _____

5. You picked up your equipment from the side counter and notice that one of the glass beakers is cracked and broken.

   _____

   _____

6. You accidentally spilled some chemicals on your hand and begin to rub your eyes.

   _____

   _____

   _____

7. After you are done with the lab, the hot beaker is still sitting on the hot plate. You need to start cleaning up.

   _____

   _____

Why is the reproduction of cells important?

Use with textbook pages 6–13.

Reproduction

Reproduction is one of the most important characteristics of living things. It ensures sustainability and continuity of a species. In order for a species to continue to exist from one generation to the next, individuals of that species must produce offspring to replace individuals that eventually die.

Asexual and Sexual Reproduction

There are two kinds of reproduction: asexual and sexual. **Asexual reproduction** occurs when a single parent produces offspring that are genetically identical to itself. In **sexual reproduction**, two parents are required to produce the offspring. Unlike asexual reproduction, the offspring are not genetically identical to the parents because they inherit half of their genetic information from one parent and half from the other. Figure 1.4 on page 10 of the textbook shows how asexual reproduction and sexual reproduction bring about different outcomes.

DNA

Parents pass on their genetic material to their offspring in a molecule called **deoxyribonucleic acid (DNA)**. The figure below shows the components of the double-stranded DNA molecule. DNA usually exists in a condensed form called **chromatin** and is found in the nucleus of the cell. The sequence of **nucleotides**, the building blocks of DNA, determines the physical characteristics and behaviour of the organism. When an organism undergoes cell division, chromatin is condensed into **chromosomes**. Copies of the chromosomes are transferred from the parents to the offspring during reproduction. The figure below shows the double helix structure of DNA with the nucleotides linking the strands.

Salmon and Sustainability

Use with textbook pages 8–9.

Use the following reading passage to answer questions 1 to 8.

Salmon is found in the streams, rivers, lakes, and coastal waters of B.C. It plays the important ecological role of a keystone species in the marine and terrestrial ecosystems of this province. It is not only a major food source for First Peoples of B.C., but also feeds a variety of different animals, from the grizzly bear to the bald eagle.

Salmon is deeply embedded in the culture, legends, artwork, traditional beliefs, and ceremonial celebrations of First Peoples. It is highly respected spiritually and seen as a symbol of abundance and prosperity in aboriginal culture. During spawning season, First Peoples gather to witness and celebrate nature's circle of life. At the end of the salmon's life cycle, the mature salmon returns to its original spawning grounds to produce, lay, and fertilize eggs for the next generation. Female salmon lay their eggs in the water while male salmon release their sperm over the eggs in a process called external fertilization. The mature adult salmon then die, providing food sources for many animals in the ecosystem.

To prevent overfishing and the depletion of the salmon run, First Peoples elders pass on their traditional ecological knowledge about sustainable methods of fishing and harvesting. This will ensure sustainability and continuity for their way of life for many generations to come.

1. Asking Questions

While reading the three paragraphs above, stop to ask who, what, when, where, why, and how questions. Write these six questions down. See if your questions are answered in the text. If they are not, reread the paragraphs to see if you misunderstood a concept. This will allow you to make connections beyond the text.

a) Who _____

b) What _____

c) When _____

d) Where _____

e) Why _____

f) How _____

2. Identifying the Main Idea and Details

To identify the main ideas, skim the text to get a sense of the content. Facts and examples provide details to help reinforce the main idea. Draw a spider map to show the main idea and the details that support it. Then compare your spider map with a partner and discuss why you chose to include certain details.

3. What suggests that salmon can exist in both fresh water and salt water?

_____

_____

4. What do you think a "keystone species" is? What do you think would happen to the ecosystem if salmon were depleted?

_____

_____

5. What type of reproduction occurs in salmon? Give evidence for this.

_____

_____

6. How do First Peoples ensure sustainability of salmon?

_____

7. Find out more about the different fishing methods that First Peoples use. How long have they been using these practices?

_____

8. Do some research to find out how salmon show the interconnectedness of different food webs in B.C. ecosystems.

The Importance of Reproduction

Use with textbook pages 10–11.

1. Making Connections to Visuals

Look at the three photographs showing different strategies for reproduction in Figure 1.3 on page 10 of the textbook. Read the introductory paragraph describing the three photographs. Then think about and answer the following questions:

a) Based on my prior knowledge, what personal connection can I make to the photograph of the hummingbird and the flower?

_____

_____

b) What can I learn about the photograph of the two birds performing a courtship ritual from the caption and the accompanying text in the paragraph?

_____

_____

c) What do the three photographs not show about reproduction?

_____

_____

d) With a partner, discuss your answers to the three questions above.

2. Previewing Text Features

Preview features of the text such as definitions of key terms that are boldfaced or italicized. These features give you clues about the most important concepts in the text. For example, the key terms **DNA** and **chromosome** are boldfaced in the paragraphs and defined in the margin of the page. In addition to these terms, there are words that are italicized such as *nucleotides*, *DNA sequence*, and *chromatin*. Include all the boldfaced and italicized words in your study notes for the next step.

3. Making Study Notes

Make study notes for the text on page 11 of the textbook to help you identify the main ideas about DNA. Use your own words to explain and summarize details of the concepts covered in the text. Choose from the following formats to help you learn and connect the concepts:

- point form
- short sentences
- graphic organizers

Asexual and Sexual Reproduction

Use with textbook pages 10–11.

1. Complete the compare and contrast graphic organizer for asexual reproduction and sexual reproduction.

COMPARE AND CONTRAST

Main Topic
Reproduction

Subtopic
Asexual reproduction

Subtopic
Sexual reproduction

ALIKE

DIFFERENT

2. Identify whether the reproductive strategy in each scenario is related to asexual reproduction or sexual reproduction. Give reasons for your answer.

a) A female komodo dragon lays a clutch of eggs that requires fertilization from a male dragon.

_____

b) A male great blue heron carries out elegant courtship displays to attract a female heron to his nest.

_____

c) A purple Pisaster sea star is chopped into two pieces, but is able to regenerate into two sea stars.

_____

d) The houseplant "mother of thousands" produces new miniature plantlets from its leaves.

_____

e) Male wood frogs make distinctive duck-like quacking sounds all day and night to let female wood frogs know that they are interested in breeding.

_____

f) A female copperhead snake in captivity gives birth to a litter of snakes without fertilization of her eggs. The offspring are genetically identical to their mother.

_____

g) During the fall rut, bulls (male moose) will fight with their antlers to determine the dominant male in the group. The noise from the sparring moose will attract the cows (female moose). The bulls will let out grunting noises to let the cows know that they are interested in mating.

_____

Organizational Levels of DNA

Use with textbook pages 10–11.

1. Label the diagram below showing the organizational level of DNA with the following terms: chromatin, chromosome, DNA helix, DNA sequence, nucleotides.

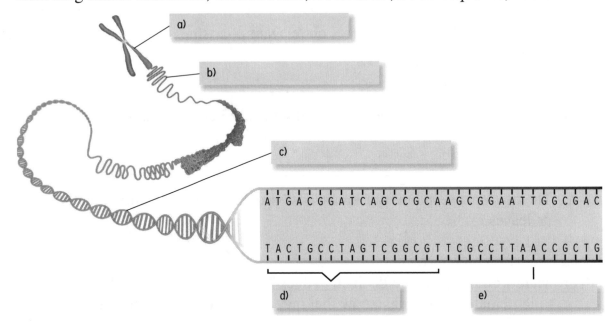

2. Describe each of the following parts.

	Organization Level of DNA	Description
a)	Chromatin	
b)	Chromosome	
c)	DNA helix	
d)	DNA sequence	
e)	Nucleotide	

3. Describe how each of the following are related to each other.

a) chromatin and DNA

_____

b) chromosomes and reproduction

_____

c) DNA sequence and nucleotides

_____

1.1 Assessment

Match each term on the left with the best description on the right. Each description may be used only once.

Term	Description
1. _____ DNA	A. requires two parents and produces genetically different offspring
2. _____ chromosome	B. requires only one parent to produce genetically identical offspring
3. _____ sexual reproduction	C. is a double-stranded molecule carrying an organism's genetic information
4. _____ asexual reproduction	D. is a condensed structure that is passed on from the parents to the offspring during reproduction

Circle the letter of the best answer for questions 5 to 17.

5. The Vancouver Aquarium introduced the Ocean Wise program to educate and promote sustainable seafood choices. Which of the following do you think a program like this would help reduce?

I	the extinction of marine species
II	the depletion of natural resources
III	the amount of seafood people ate

   A. I and II only   **C.** II and III only

   B. I and III only   **D.** I, II, and III

6. Which of the following is an example of a sustainable practice?

   A. cutting down trees without planting new seedlings

   B. growing and harvesting of crops that allow future crop yields

   C. clearing land and making the soil unsuitable for agriculture use

   D. fishing methods that will diminish the entire population of salmon

7. Sustainability of organisms is dependent on the ability of the organisms to

   A. obtain nutrients.

   B. grow and develop.

   C. migrate to different habitat.

   D. pass on their genetic information to future generations.

8. "Continuity" is dependent on whether living things

   A. grow.

   B. reproduce.

   C. use energy.

   D. respond to stimuli.

9. If continuity did not occur for a species, then that species would face the threat of

   A. isolation.

   B. extinction.

   C. habitat loss.

   D. propagation.

10. Which of the following is associated with asexual reproduction?

I	one parent
II	genetic variation between offspring
III	offspring have the exact genetic makeup as the parent

   A. I and II only

   B. I and III only

   C. II and III only

   D. I, II, and III

11. Which of the following is an example of asexual reproduction?

   A. a *paramecium* splits into two new organisms

   B. a black-capped chickadee uses a variety of songs to attract mates

   C. a checkerspot butterfly transfers pollen from one wildflower to another

   D. a male red fox successfully courts a vixen, resulting in a litter of four kits

12. A horse has 64 chromosomes. During sexual reproduction, how many chromosomes does each of the parents contribute to the offspring?

	Male Horse	Female Horse
A.	32	32
B.	32	64
C.	64	32
D.	64	64

13. What are the building blocks of DNA called?

   A. sugars

   B. chromatins

   C. nucleotides

   D. chromosomes

14. What do asexual reproduction and sexual reproduction have in common?

  A. They both require the individual finding a mate.

  B. They both result in genetically identical individuals.

  C. They both involve the parent inheriting DNA from the offspring.

  D. They both involve the passing on of genetic material to future generations.

15. Which of the following describes the results of most cases of sexual reproduction?

I	offspring are genetically different from parents
II	offspring are genetically identical to both parents
III	offspring are genetically different from each other

  A. I and II only

  B. I and III only

  C. II and III only

  D. I, II, and III

16. Chromosomes consist of which of the following?

I	DNA
II	nucleotides
III	A, C, T, and G

  A. I and II only

  B. I and III only

  C. II and III only

  D. I, II, and III

17. What determines the colour of a grizzly bear's fur?

  A. the DNA sequence

  B. the type of nucleotides

  C. the size of the chromatin

  D. the number of chromosomes

18. Complete the Venn diagram to compare and contrast chromosome and chromatin.

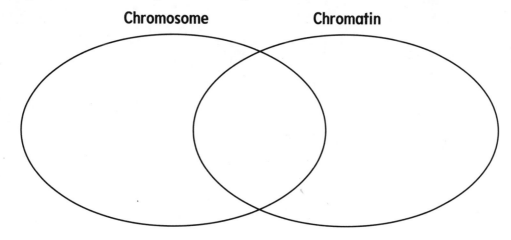

Chromosome   Chromatin

What are different ways that living things reproduce asexually?

Use with textbook pages 20–35.

Binary Fission

In **binary fission**, a *parent cell* splits into two identical *daughter cells* that have the same genetic material as the parent. Binary fission is a form of asexual reproduction that occurs in bacteria. Refer to Figure 1.7 on page 23 to see what happens during binary fission. What steps are involved in this process?

Cell Cycle

Eukaryotic cells reproduce to replace damaged or older cells. They do this through the cell cycle, which is divided into two stages: the growth and development stage and the division stage. The pie chart in Figure 1.10 on page 27 of the textbook shows the relative amount of time a cell spends in each phase during its life. The growth and development stage is called **interphase**. During this phase, the cell grows bigger, the organelles increase in number, and DNA is duplicated in preparation for cell division. The division stage includes mitosis and cytokinesis. **Mitosis** is the division of the nucleus, while **cytokinesis** is the division of the cytoplasm. Mitosis has four phases: prophase, metaphase, anaphase, and telophase. During **prophase**, the nuclear membrane disappears and DNA condenses further into chromosomes. Spindle fibres start to form. These spindle fibres move the chromosomes to the middle of the cell in **metaphase**. During **anaphase**, the spindle fibres pull the chromosomes to the two ends of the cell. The chromosomes have reached the two ends of the cell in **telophase** and the nuclear membrane forms around each complete set of chromosomes. The cell then undergoes cytokinesis, where the cytoplasm splits in half. The end product is two new daughter cells that are identical to the parent cell and to each other. The figure below shows interphase, the phases of mitosis, and cytokinesis.

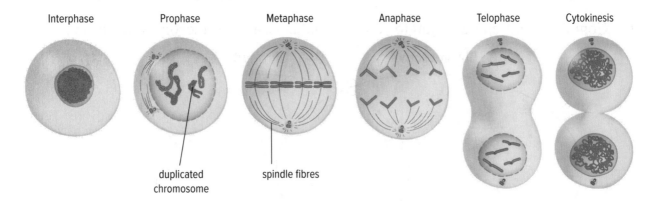

Interphase   Prophase   Metaphase   Anaphase   Telophase   Cytokinesis

duplicated chromosome   spindle fibres

Budding

In **budding**, a small **bud** grows from the parent cell and then detaches itself. This new independent cell will grow to the size of the parent cell. This type of asexual reproduction occurs in yeast cells. The figure below shows a yeast cell dividing by budding.

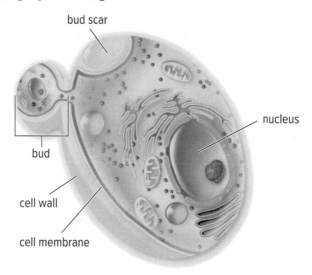

Spore Formation

Moulds and mushrooms reproduce asexually by forming **spores** that are genetically identical to the parent. The figure below shows a *sporangium* releasing some spores that will eventually grow and develop under favourable conditions.

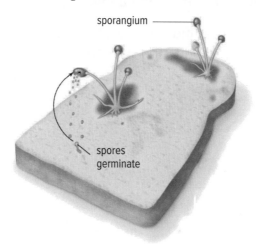

Vegetative Propagation

Plants can use **vegetative propagation** to reproduce asexually from the roots, stems, or leaves. The new plants are identical **clones** of the parent plant. Refer to Figure 1.13 on page 31 of the textbook for some examples of vegetative propagation. People use a variety of artificial vegetative propagation techniques to produce plants with desired characteristics. These techniques are described in Table 1.1 on pages 32 and 33 of the textbook.

Binary Fission

Use with textbook pages 22–23.

Use the diagram showing the reproduction of bacterial cells to answer questions 1 to 5.

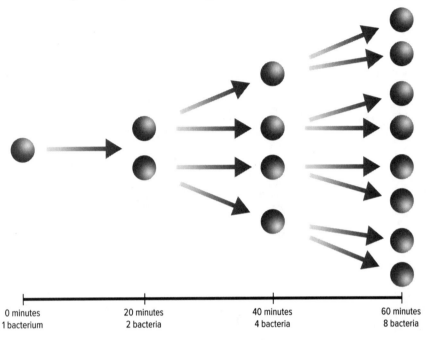

| 0 minutes | 20 minutes | 40 minutes | 60 minutes |
| 1 bacterium | 2 bacteria | 4 bacteria | 8 bacteria |

1. What type of asexual reproduction is shown above? _____

2. Bacteria double every 20 minutes under favourable conditions. Complete the following table to display the reproduction data shown in the diagram.

Time (min)	Number of Bacterial Cells
0	1
20	
40	
60 (1 h)	
80	
100	
120 (2 h)	
140	
160	
180 (3 h)	

3. Use the table on the previous page to graph the data for the first 120 minutes. What variable would go on the *x*-axis? What variable would go on the *y*-axis?

_____

_____

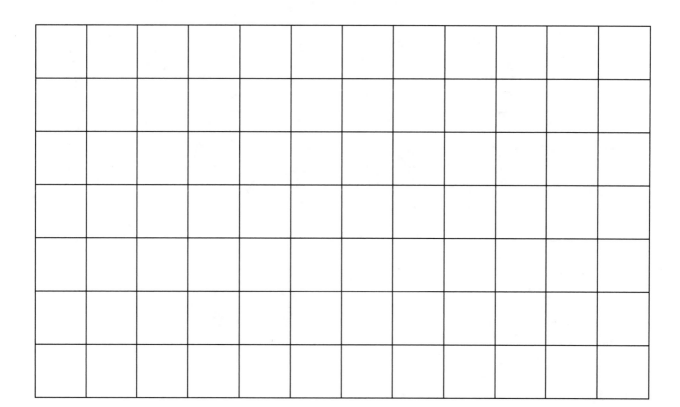

4. Describe how the graph represents the growth of the bacterial population.

_____

_____

5. Based on the reproduction rate, how many bacterial cells would you expect after

   a) 12 hours? _____

   b) 24 hours? _____

Binary Fission, Budding, and Spore Formation

Use with textbook pages 22–30.

1. Identify the type of asexual reproduction shown in each diagram.

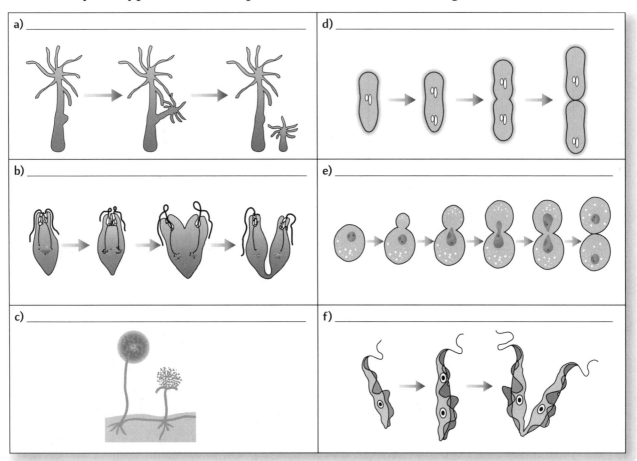

a) _____ d) _____

b) _____ e) _____

c) _____ f) _____

2. Identify the type of asexual reproduction described in each scenario.

   a) The aquatic cell of *Planctomycetes* forms a bud, which eventually becomes a
   new cell that swims. _____

   b) A unicellular green algae, *Micrasterias furcata*, divides into two equal halves
   forming two new cells. _____

   c) An amoeba grows to a certain size and then its nucleus and cytoplasm divide.
   This results in two amoebas. _____

   d) *Amanita muscaria* releases spores from under its iconic red cap with white
   warts, producing more of these poisonous B.C. toadstools.

   _____

Cell Cycle and Mitosis

Use with textbook pages 25–27.

1. Label each diagram with the corresponding stage of the cell cycle: anaphase, cytokinesis, interphase, metaphase, prophase, telophase.

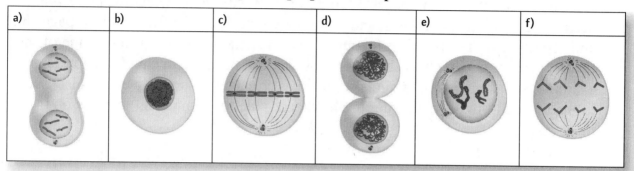

2. Which stage of the cell cycle is each of the following statements describing? Choose from the following list of terms: anaphase, cytokinesis, interphase, metaphase, prophase, telophase.

a) DNA is copied _____

b) cytoplasm divides _____

c) spindle fibres form _____

d) cell grows and develops _____

e) nuclear membrane disappears _____

f) number of organelles increases _____

g) DNA condenses into chromosomes _____

h) stage that makes up most of the life of the cell _____

i) stage where the cell carries out its life function _____

j) chromosomes line up across the middle of the cell

_____

k) nuclear membrane reappears around the chromosomes

_____

l) duplicated chromosomes have reached the opposite ends of the cell

_____

m) duplicated chromosomes are pulled apart to the opposite ends of the cell

_____

Vegetative Propagation

Use with textbook pages 31–33.

1. Previewing Text Features

Before reading the text on pages 31 to 33 of the textbook, preview the *text features* such as headings, subheadings, and main body text. Examine Table 1.1 on pages 32 and 33. Look at the title of each column and the heading for each row. Some of the text features give you clues about the most important ideas for this Concept. For example, six examples of artificial vegetative propagation techniques are discussed in the table and these techniques are boldfaced. Identify some text features on these three pages.

_____

_____

_____

_____

2. Making Study Notes on Index Cards

Making study notes on index cards for Table 1.1 on pages 32 and 33 will help you focus on the main ideas. Write your notes in your own words. Write each boldfaced word in Table 1.1 on a separate index card. On each index card, include

- the name of the artificial vegetative propagation technique,
- a sentence describing the technique,
- a list of the plants used,
- some uses for the technique.

3. Visualizing

Visualizing means forming an image in your mind based on the text that you are reading.

Look at each of the diagrams provided in Table 1.1. Look for details that make the image make sense to you. Once you have formed a final image in your mind, make a sketch of each propagation technique on your index card. Your sketch will reinforce the concepts in your study notes.

1.2 Assessment

Match each term on the left with the best description on the right. Each description may be used only once.

Term	Description
1. _____ clone	A. identical copy of a cell
2. _____ spore	B. series of events that make up the life cycle of a cell
3. _____ budding	C. structure released by a sporangium during asexual reproduction
4. _____ cell cycle	D. type of asexual reproduction where a bud forms from the parent
5. _____ binary fission	E. type of asexual reproduction where plants grow from parts of its roots, stems, or leaves
6. _____ vegetative propagation	F. type of asexual reproduction where the parent cell splits into two identical daughter cells

Circle the letter of the best answer for questions 7 to 23.

7. In which of the following methods of reproduction are the parent cells genetically identical to the daughter cells?

I	budding
II	binary fission
III	spore formation

A. I and II only   **C.** II and III only

B. I and III only   **D.** I, II, and III

8. What do budding, binary fission, and spore formation have in common?

A. They require two parent cells.

B. They require only one parent cell.

C. They produce only one daughter cell.

D. They are all forms of sexual reproduction.

9. Which of the following methods do bacteria that cause tooth decay use to reproduce?

A. budding   **C.** spore formation

B. binary fission   **D.** vegetative propagation

10. What are the end products of binary fission?

    A. two independent daughter cells that are identical to each other

    B. one daughter cell that is genetically different from the parent cell

    C. two independent daughter cells that are different from each other

    D. two daughter cells that are genetically different from the parent cell

11. Yeast reproduce by

    A. budding.   **C.** spore formation.

    B. binary fission.   **D.** vegetative propagation.

12. During budding, what is usually formed?

    A. a bud from the daughter cell

    B. new DNA from the parent cell

    C. an outgrowth from the parent cell

    D. new stems and roots from the parent cell

13. Which method does mould use to produce more mould on a piece of cheese?

    A. budding   **C.** spore formation

    B. binary fission   **D.** vegetative propagation

14. Which of the following describes when spores will grow and divide?

    A. when they are encased in a sporangium

    B. when they are in an environment with harsh conditions

    C. when they are in an environment with favourable conditions

    D. when leaves from the existing plant provide nutrients for the spores

15. Which of the following types of reproduction involve the cell cycle?

I	budding
II	binary fission
III	spore formation

    A. I and II only   **C.** II and III only

    B. I and III only   **D.** I, II, and III

16. Daffodil and tulip bulbs are planted in the fall. In the spring, these flowers grow from the bulbs. This is an example of

A. budding.

B. binary fission.

C. spore formation.

D. vegetative propagation.

17. How are potato tubers and strawberry runners similar?

A. They are not clones of the parent plant.

B. They are like stems that produce new plants.

C. They are used by plants to reproduce sexually.

D. They are like leaves that develop the roots of the new plant.

18. Which of the following techniques takes a section of the root and joins it to another plant?

A. cutting

B. grafting

C. splitting

D. air layering

19. The cell cycle consists of which of the following?

I	mitosis
II	interphase
III	cytokinesis

A. I and II only

B. I and III only

C. II and III only

D. I, II, and III

20. During which phase of mitosis do the chromosomes line up in the middle of the cell?

A. telophase

B. anaphase

C. prophase

D. metaphase

21. Copies of DNA are made during

    A. prophase.   **C.** telophase.

    B. anaphase.   **D.** interphase.

22. Which of the following occurs during anaphase?

    A. spindle fibres form

    B. nuclear membrane disappears

    C. chromosomes are pulled to the opposite ends of the cell

    D. nuclear membrane reappears around the two new sets of chromosomes

23. The cytoplasm is divided to produce two new cells during

    A. prophase.   **C.** interphase.

    B. anaphase.   **D.** cytokinesis.

24. Complete the following spider map for the phases of mitosis. Describe what happens during each phase of mitosis.

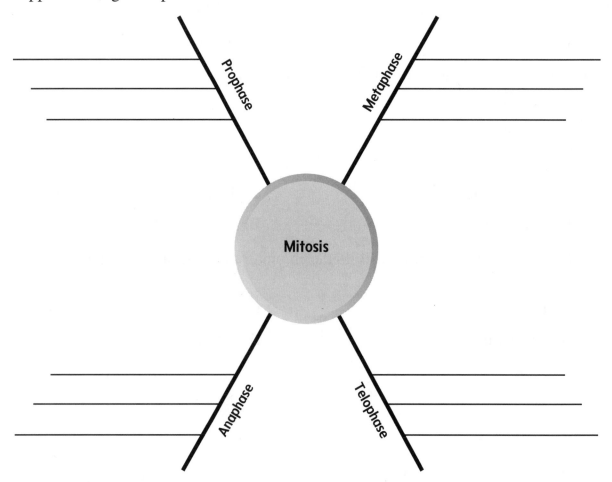

How do living things sexually reproduce?

Use with textbook pages 44–57.

Gametes

Gametes, also known as sex cells, are required during sexual reproduction. The male gamete is the *sperm* and the female gamete is the *egg*. The sperm combines with the egg to form a *zygote* in a process called **fertilization**. Half of the genetic material of the zygote comes from the sperm and the other half comes from the egg.   The figure below shows the union of the egg and the sperm.

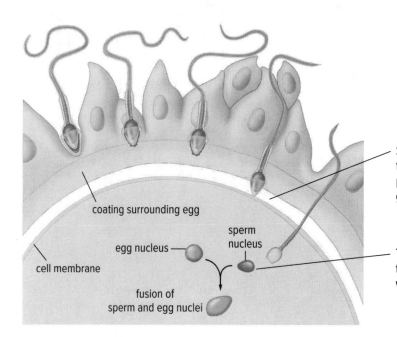

coating surrounding egg

cell membrane

egg nucleus

sperm nucleus

fusion of sperm and egg nuclei

Sperm cells reach a jelly-like coating surrounding the egg cell and release substances that digest a path through the coating. This helps sperm cells get closer to the cell membrane of the egg.

The head of one sperm cell eventually enters the egg cell, where the sperm nucleus fuses with the egg nucleus.

Haploid and Diploid

Gametes have half the normal number of chromosomes and are said to be **haploid**. When two gametes combine, they form a cell that is **diploid**, having a full set of chromosomes. These chromosomes are paired and are called *homologous chromosomes*. In the pair, one chromosome comes from the female parent and the other comes from the male parent. Figure 1.19 on page 49 shows the difference between haploid and diploid cells.

Meiosis

During **meiosis**, a diploid cell undergoes two consecutive cell divisions to produce four haploid cells. These four cells are the gametes that will be involved in sexual reproduction. The figure below shows the first cell division.

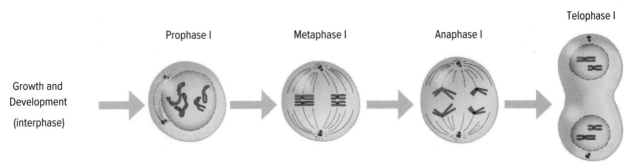

Once the cell has divided once, the two daughter cells each divide again. The figure below shows the second cell division.

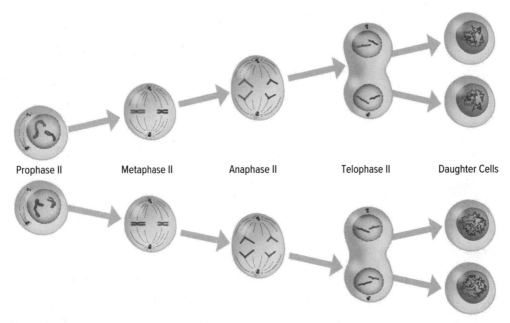

Human Development

After fertilization, the single-celled *zygote* undergoes a series of cell divisions to become an *embryo*. The embryo continues to divide, grow, and develop into a fetus. Table 1.2 on page 53 of the textbook shows the key prenatal developments over nine months.

Sexual Reproduction in Other Organisms

Other organisms reproduce through sexual reproduction as well. Some fertilized eggs develop inside the female's body, while others develop outside the body. In plants, seeds and pollen are involved in pollination and fertilization. Refer to Figure 1.23 on pages 54 and 55 of the textbook to review the different ways organisms reproduce.

Gametes

Use with textbook pages 46–48.

1. Label the diagram below.

    a) Use the following terms for parts a) to f): **female chromosome, male chromosome, egg, fertilization, sperm, zygote**.

    b) Use the following terms for parts i), ii), and iii), **diploid, haploid**.

    c) Identify the method (mitosis or meiosis) that produces the cell. Label boxes x), y), and z).

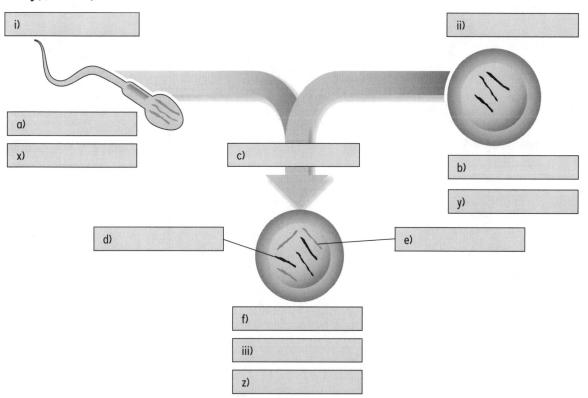

2. Determine how many chromosomes are in the gametes and body cells of these organisms.

	Organism	Number of Chromosomes in the Gametes	Number of Chromosomes in the Body Cells
a)	Human, *Homo sapiens*	23	
b)	Sea otter, *Enhydra lutris*		38
c)	Spirit bear, *Ursus americanus*	37	
d)	Chinook salmon, *Oncorhynchus tshawytscha*		68
e)	Red fox, *Vulpes vulpes*	17	

Meiosis

Use with textbook pages 49–51.

1. What is the purpose of meiosis?

_____

2. Label each diagram with the corresponding stage of meiosis: **anaphase I, anaphase II, interphase, metaphase I, metaphase II, prophase I, prophase II, telophase I, telophase II.**

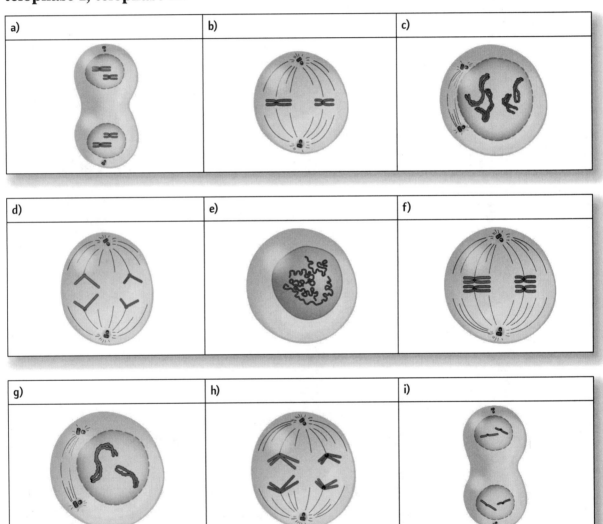

3. Which stage of meiosis is each of the following statements describing? Choose from the following list of terms: **anaphase I, anaphase II, metaphase I, metaphase II, prophase I, prophase II, telophase I, telophase II, interphase**.

a) two nuclei form _____

b) four nuclei form _____

c) cell is growing and developing _____

d) homologous chromosomes pair up _____

e) cell divides into two daughter cells _____

f) cell divides into four daughter cells _____

g) DNA condenses into chromosomes _____

h) nuclear membrane starts to disappear _____

i) chromosomes line up in the middle of the cell _____

j) DNA exists as chromosomes but not homologous pairs

_____

k) chromosomes separate and move to the ends of the cell

_____

l) each nuclei formed has a complete copy of the cell's DNA

_____

m) nuclear membrane starts to disappear and homologous chromosomes pair

_____

n) homologous chromosome pairs separate and start to move to the two ends of the cell _____

o) spindle fibres line up the homologous chromosome pairs in the middle of the cell _____

Human Development

Use with textbook pages 52–53.

1. Skim, Scan, and Study

As you read Concept 3, determine the purpose for reading pages 52 and 53. Review the three different purposes for reading and the different approaches.

Purpose	Reading Approach
Preview the text to get an idea of what the text contains.	Skim: Read the text over quickly.
Find specific information.	Scan: Read the text somewhat quickly.
Learn a new concept.	Study: Read the text slowly.

You can determine the reading approach by the placement and features of the text. For example, text that is placed in the introductory paragraph is often meant to stimulate interest and may not include important concepts. Text with boldfaced words should be read slowly.

Choose the reading approach that you think should be used for each of the following tasks and explain why. Skim, scan, or study to complete each task and determine whether the approach chosen is appropriate.

a) Get a general idea about Figure 1.22.

_____

_____

b) Determine when the embryonic stage and the fetal stage occur during prenatal development.

_____

_____

c) Learn what happens during each of the nine months in prenatal development.

_____

_____

2. Using Graphic Organizers

Summarizing concepts with a graphic organizer can help you comprehend and remember concepts better. Use lines and arrows to show sequence relationships. Create a graphic organizer of your choice to summarize the events that occur during prenatal development.

Different Types of Sexual Reproduction

Use with textbook pages 54–55.

1. Summarizing

Summarizing means to restate the main ideas in your own words. A summary can be in point form, in sentence form, or graphic form. For example, the first row of the table below shows you how to create a summary of the concepts covered on pages 54 and 55. Complete the rest of the table.

Section of the Text	Main Topic	What the Text Says about the Main Topic	Supporting Details
Page 54, statement 1 about mammals	Development inside the female occurs in mammals.	"Development from fertilized egg to offspring of most mammals occurs inside the female, who is also the source of nourishment."	• A cow carries a young elk inside her and gives birth. • The fetus of a sea otter develops inside the female sea otter. • A baby orca grows inside the mother.
Page 54, statements 2–5 about insects			
Page 54, statement 6 about fungi			
Page 55, statements 1–2 involving eggs			
Page 55, statements 3–4 about plants			

1.3 Assessment

Match each term on the left with the best description on the right. Each description may be used only once.

Term	Description
1. ____ diploid	A. a sex cell
2. ____ gamete	B. union of the egg and sperm
3. ____ haploid	C. has a full set of chromosomes
4. ____ meiosis	D. process that produces haploid cells
5. ____ fertilization	E. has half the number of chromosomes

Circle the letter of the best answer for questions 6 to 20.

6. What does the female parent contribute in sexual reproduction?

   A. an egg

   B. a sperm

   C. a zygote

   D. an ovary

7. Where are sperm produced?

   A. in the brain

   B. in the uterus

   C. in the testes

   D. in the ovaries

8. How are eggs and sperm similar?

   A. They are diploid cells.

   B. They are haploid cells.

   C. They are produced by mitosis.

   D. They are produced by fertilization.

9. What is formed when a sperm fertilizes an egg?

   A. a zygote

   B. a gamete

   C. a haploid cell

   D. a homologous chromosome

10. The Vancouver Island marmot has 40 chromosomes in its body cells. How many chromosomes would you expect a male marmot to have in its sperm cells?

    A. 10 chromosomes

    B. 20 chromosomes

    C. 40 chromosomes

    D. 80 chromosomes

11. The gametes of a white-tailed deer have 35 chromosomes. When the sperm of a white-tailed buck combines with the egg of a white-tailed doe, how many chromosomes would the zygote have?

 A. 17.5 chromosomes

 B. 35 chromosomes

 C. 70 chromosomes

 D. 140 chromosomes

12. What usually combines during fertilization?

 A. zygotes   **C.** gametes

 B. embryos   **D.** diploid cells

13. Which of the following shows the series of events in human development?

 A. embryo → zygote → sperm + egg → fetus

 B. sperm + egg → fetus → zygote → embryo

 C. zygote → fetus → embryo → sperm + egg

 D. sperm + egg → zygote → embryo → fetus

14. What allows a zygote to develop into an embryo?

 A. the zygote dividing by mitosis over several weeks

 B. the zygote dividing by meiosis over several weeks

 C. the zygote developing into gametes through mitosis over several weeks

 D. the zygote fusing with another zygote and then dividing by meiosis over several weeks

15. Which of the following is associated with sexual reproduction?

I	meiosis
II	pollination
III	fertilization

 A. I and II only

 B. I and III only

 C. II and III only

 D. I, II, and III

16. Which of the following applies to meiosis?

	Number of Cell Divisions	Number of Daughter Cells
A.	2	4
B.	2	2
C.	1	4
D.	1	2

17. Paired chromosomes are called

    A. diploid.   **C.** asexual.

    B. haploid.   **D.** homologous.

18. During which phase of meiosis are the homologous chromosome pairs lined up in the middle of the cell?

    A. prophase I   **C.** telophase I

    B. anaphase I   **D.** metaphase I

19. Four nuclei form around the sets of chromosomes during

    A. prophase II.   **C.** telophase II.

    B. anaphase II.   **D.** metaphase II.

20. When is the nuclear membrane disappearing during meiosis?

    A. interphase and prophase I   **C.** telophase I and telophase II

    B. prophase I and prophase II   **D.** metaphase I and anaphase II

21. Complete the following Frayer model for gametes.

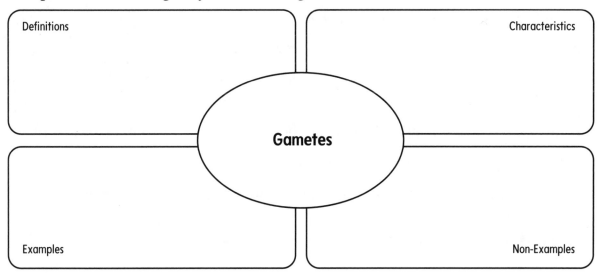

How does reproduction contribute to the variety of life on Earth?

Use with textbook pages 62-69.

Advantages of Asexual Reproduction

There are several advantages to asexual reproduction.

1. Only one parent is required, so there is no need to find a mate.

2. The parent can produce the offspring quickly.

3. Offspring can reproduce shortly after they are formed.

4. Offspring are genetically identical to the parent and can survive in the same environment as their parent.

Disadvantages of Asexual Reproduction

Since organisms produced by asexual reproduction are all genetically identical, they will be affected by environmental changes in the same way. The lack of genetic diversity can make them vulnerable to changes in environmental conditions and they may not survive.

Advantages of Sexual Reproduction

Sexual reproduction provides **genetic variation** within a population. Individuals are different from each other because of their genetic makeup. Even within the same family, you may notice that siblings look similar to each other, but have unique characteristics that distinguish them from each other. This is because each sibling inherits a different combination of genetic information from each of their parents. If the environment changes, the genetic variation within a population means that certain individuals might be more likely to survive and reproduce, passing these traits on to their offspring.

Disadvantages of Sexual Reproduction

There are several disadvantages to sexual reproduction.

1. Organisms need to find a mate to reproduce. This might expose the organisms to diseases, predators, competition, and other unsafe conditions.

2. Sexual reproduction takes longer and therefore fewer offspring are produced.

3. Offspring take a while to mature before they can reproduce.

4. A lot of time and energy goes into raising offspring before they are able to take care of themselves.

These disadvantages limit the rate of population growth.

Advantages and Disadvantages of Reproduction

Use with textbook pages 64–67.

1. Previewing Text Features

Before reading pages 64 to 67, preview the features of the text. Major text features include headings, subheadings, and main body text. Other text features include definitions of key terms.

Some text features give you clues about the most important ideas in the text. When studying for a test, use these features to find the important terms and concepts.

2. Monitoring Comprehension

As you read, stop after each paragraph to check your understanding. Place a small sticky note beside each paragraph. Put a ✓ if you comprehend the concepts covered and put an ✗ if you do not understand or are confused about the content. For the paragraphs that you *do* understand, rephrase the main ideas in your own words. For the paragraphs that you *do not* understand, use the following strategies:

- reread the paragraph
- identify the part that is confusing you or that you do not understand
- if a key term is unclear, look up its definition in the glossary
- if a concept is unclear or confusing, look at Figures 1.24, 1.25, and 1.26 to see if they can help you understand the concept.

3. Visualizing

Visualizing means forming an image in your mind based on the text that you are reading.

a) Select a section in the text. What is the main idea?

_____

b) What image forms in your mind for this main idea? Explain how this image connects to the main idea.

_____

_____

c) Make a sketch of your image.

Asexual Reproduction or Sexual Reproduction

Use with textbook pages 64–67.

Use the following reading passage to answer questions 1 to 9.

Many organisms primarily reproduce asexually, but are also capable of reproducing sexually. Examples include plants, bacteria, aphids, yeast, mould, hydra, sea anemone, and sea stars. They carry out asexual reproduction when resources, like food supply, are plentiful and environmental conditions are favourable. Asexual reproduction allows the population to increase exponentially to take advantage of the abundant food sources. This form of reproduction is the most efficient way for these organisms to create genetic clones of the parents and to pass on their genetic information to the next generation.

When environmental conditions are unfavourable, these organisms will switch to sexual reproduction. This adaptation is seen when food sources are scarce, the climate is hostile, parasites or diseases are present, or there are any other changes in conditions that threaten the species' survival. These organisms need the genetic variation that sexual reproduction offers in order to increase their offspring's chances of surviving under these conditions. Many organisms and plants have adaptations to deal with changing environments that become unsuitable for many of the population. These include producing seeds, spores, and pupae to help them get through these conditions.

1. Identifying the Main Idea and Details

To identify the main idea, skim the text to get a sense of the content. Facts and examples provide details to help reinforce the main idea. Draw a spider map to show the main idea and the details that support it. Then compare your spider map with a partner and discuss why you chose to include certain details.

2. What method of reproduction do most organisms that can reproduce both asexually and sexually use most of the time?

_____

3. When do organisms carry out asexual reproduction?

_____

4. What is one advantage of asexual reproduction?

_____

5. What advantage does an "asexual" organism gain by reproducing sexually?

_____

_____

6. What factor usually causes an organism to switch from asexual reproduction to sexual reproduction?

_____

7. List two examples of when environmental conditions are unfavourable.

_____

_____

8. List some adaptations that plants and animals have to help them get through harsh conditions.

_____

_____

_____

9. Asking Questions

While reading the two paragraphs above, stop to ask who, what, when, where, why, and how questions. Write these six questions down. See if your questions are answered in the text. If they are not, reread the paragraphs to see if you misunderstood a concept. This will allow you to make connections beyond the text.

a) Who _____

b) What _____

c) When _____

d) Where _____

e) Why _____

f) How _____

Advantages of Asexual and Sexual Reproduction

Use with textbook pages 64–67.

Identify whether the statement is an advantage of asexual reproduction or sexual reproduction.

1. requires only one parent

_____

2. produces offspring that are unique

_____

3. provides greater genetic variation

_____

4. requires less energy to reproduce

_____

5. takes offspring less time to mature

_____

6. requires no energy to find a mate

_____

7. produces offspring that are genetically identical to the parent

_____

8. provides a fast and efficient way of producing large amounts of offspring

_____

9. produces individuals that are able to adapt to changing environment

_____

10. allows population to grow exponentially and outcompete other organisms for

resources

_____

11. provides an increased probability of surviving if there are changes in the
environment because individuals are genetically different

_____

Disadvantages of Asexual and Sexual Reproduction

Use with textbook pages 64–67.

Identify whether the statement is a disadvantage of asexual reproduction or sexual reproduction.

1. results in no genetic diversity _____

2. produces fewer offspring _____

3. takes offspring a longer time to mature _____

4. produces offspring that are genetic clones _____

5. takes a longer time for a population to grow _____

6. provides no genetic variation among the offspring

   _____

7. requires gametes to contact each other in order for offspring to form

   _____

8. requires parents to invest a lot of time and energy to raise offspring

   _____

9. provides limited ability to adapt to changing environmental conditions

   _____

10. means that finding a mate may expose individuals to predators and diseases

    _____

11. means that unfavourable environmental conditions can wipe out the entire
    population _____

12. means that searching for a mate can result in injury or death due to competition
    with other potential suitors _____

13. requires a long time for organisms to grow and develop to the stage where they can
    reproduce themselves _____

14. means that individuals are more vulnerable and susceptible to diseases and parasites
    because they are all clones and respond to the disease in the same way

    _____

1.4 Assessment

Match each term on the left with the best description on the right. Each description may be used only once.

Term	Description
1. ____ genetic variation	A. type of reproduction that requires one parent
2. ____ sexual reproduction	B. type of reproduction that requires two parents
3. ____ asexual reproduction	C. DNA sequences are different for each individual in a species

Circle the letter of the best answer for questions 4 to 10.

4. Asexual reproduction requires

   A. two parents.

   B. two gametes.

   C. only one parent.

   D. only one gamete.

5. Which of the following is an advantage of asexual reproduction?

   A. it occurs really slowly

   B. it allows the population to grow rapidly

   C. it takes time for the offspring to mature before they can reproduce

   D. it allows the parents to pass on 50% of their genetic material to their offspring

6. A lack of genetic diversity from asexual reproduction means that

   A. all the gametes are clones of each other.

   B. all the offspring are genetically identical to each other.

   C. the offspring did not inherit any genetic materials from the parents.

   D. the population have individuals with different combinations of DNA sequences.

7. A deadly fungal disease hit an apple orchard that was grown by asexual reproduction using grafting. What would you expect to happen to the rest of the crop if one apple tree was vulnerable to that disease?

   A. All the apple trees would grow rapidly, producing more apples.

   B. All the other apple trees would be resistant to the fungal disease.

   C. All the other apple trees would adapt so that they could survive the disease.

   D. All the other apple trees would be equally vulnerable to the disease and could be wiped out.

8. Sexual reproduction promotes

    A. genetic diversity.

    B. susceptibility to disease.

    C. the production of clones.

    D. the same features in all the individuals.

9. Which of the following explains why finding a mate for sexual reproduction is a disadvantage?

I	It is time consuming to look for that mate.
II	It exposes the organism to potential predators.
III	It may involve competition with other organisms for that mate and result in injury or death.

    A. I and II only

    B. I and III only

    C. II and III only

    D. I, II, and III

10. Which of the following is a disadvantage of sexual reproduction?

    A. No gametes are required.

    B. Fewer offspring are produced.

    C. It is an energy efficient way to produce offspring.

    D. A shorter time is needed to produce the offspring.

11. Complete the T-chart for sexual reproduction showing its advantages and disadvantages.

Sexual Reproduction

Advantages	Disadvantages

What happens when there is an error in meiosis?

What's the Issue?

In humans, meiosis is the cell division that produces gametes with 23 chromosomes. If a mistake occurs during meiosis, a gamete may have an extra copy of an entire chromosome. When this gamete fuses with a normal gamete, the individual ends up with 47 chromosomes, instead of the typical 46 chromosomes. There will then be an extra chromosome in every cell in the body. In most cases, the incorrect number of chromosomes results in miscarriages in humans. In other cases, individuals with this chromosomal abnormality are born with birth defects, severe disabilities, and health problems.

The most common chromosomal abnormalities include trisomy 21, trisomy 13, trisomy 18, and sex-chromosome trisomies. Trisomy is the condition where a person has an extra copy of a chromosome. It can be detected by analyzing the individual's karyotype. Trisomies 13 and 18 are rare in humans because the fetuses have severe developmental problems. They usually end in miscarriages because the fetuses fail to develop to birth.

In trisomy 21, there are three copies of chromosome 21. This is the primary cause of Down syndrome. Individuals with this condition have birth defects, severe disabilities, and a shorter life expectancy. The risk of having a child with Down syndrome increases as the mother ages. Trisomy 21 is due to a mistake that occurs when the chromosomes fail to separate during meiosis. In most cases, an extra chromosome 21 ends up in the gamete, resulting in the gamete having 24 chromosomes. When this gamete undergoes fertilization, the resulting zygote has 47 chromosomes. As the zygote divides and becomes a fetus, all the body cells in the fetus will have an extra chromosome.

The other types of trisomies involve sex chromosomes. Humans typically have 23 pairs, or 46 chromosomes. The 23rd pair is known as the sex chromosomes. Females usually have XX and males usually have XY. In sex-chromosome trisomies (XXX, XXY, and XYY) a pair of sex chromosomes do not separate properly during gamete formation. Individuals with these chromosomal abnormalities have an extra sex chromosome in their gametes. Compared to the other chromosomal abnormalities, sex-chromosome trisomies have less severe results. Individuals with these conditions may experience reduced fertility or sterility.

A mistake in meiosis can cause a chromosomal imbalance. In some cases, the results are devastating and fatal. In other cases, the individuals may live relatively normal lives with some serious health consequences.

Dig Deeper

Collaborate with your classmates to explore one or more of these questions—or generate your own questions to explore.

1. a) During what phase of meiosis would you expect the error to occur resulting in trisomy 21? Explain.

   b) Describe the results if the mistake occurred in the first cell division of meiosis.

   c) Describe the results if the mistake occurred in the second cell division of meiosis.

2. Research the correlation between the incidences of Down syndrome and maternal age. Create a graph to show your findings.

3. Individuals born with trisomy 21 are more likely to survive than individuals with trisomy 13, who usually die within the first few weeks of birth. Form a hypothesis to explain why this is so.

4. Individuals with sex-chromosome trisomies like XXX, XXY, and XYY usually have reduced fertility and sterility problems. What inference can you make?

5. What type of prenatal screening is available to diagnose and detect some of the chromosomal abnormalities? Is the screening necessary? Are there any risks associated with the screening?

6. a) What are some ethical considerations surrounding prenatal screening and diagnosis of trisomies and sex-chromosome trisomies?

   b) What are the incidence rates of trisomy 13, trisomy 21, and sex-chromosome trisomies. Do the incidence rate and risks associated with screening affect your answer to part a)?

How and why do we study matter?

Use with textbook pages 86-95.

Pure Substances and Mixtures

Matter is anything that has mass and volume. It can be classified into two categories: pure substances and mixtures. A **pure substance** consists of one type of particle and cannot be separated by physical means. A pure substance can further be divided into two groups: elements and compounds. An **element** is made up of one type of atom. When atoms of two or more elements combine, they form a **compound**.

A **mixture** consists of two or more types of particles and can be separated by physical means. There are two types of mixtures: homogeneous and heterogeneous. The different substances in a **homogeneous mixture** are mixed uniformly throughout, and the different components within the mixture are not visible. A **heterogeneous mixture** has components that are distinctly visible.

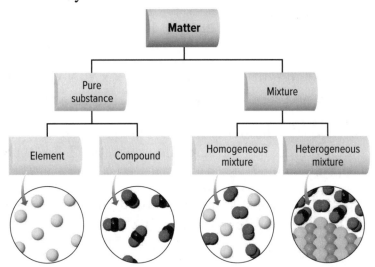

Physical and Chemical Properties

Physical properties describe matter according to characteristics that are observed and measured. **Chemical properties** show the ability of matter to react with each other to form new substances. When a new substance is formed, a **chemical reaction** has occurred. Table 2.1 on page 89 in the textbook provides a list of physical and chemical properties.

Safety in the Lab

Review the safety icons and Workplace Hazardous Materials Information System (WHMIS) symbol shown in Figure 2.4 on page 91 of the textbook. The blue **safety icons** show the important procedures that should be followed before conducting a lab investigation. The **WHMIS symbols** are pictograms that identify the potential hazards that are associated with substances used in a lab. Refer to Figure 2.5 on pages 92 and 93 in the textbook to review the different safety rules in the science classroom.

Pure Substances and Mixtures

Use with textbook pages 88–90.

Use the following reading passage to answer questions 1 to 3.

Your alarm goes off at 7:00 a.m. and you roll out of bed. You make your way to the kitchen and pour yourself a glass of pulpy orange juice. The sour taste helps you wake up. You walk over to the cupboard and reach for your favourite granola cereal that has cranberries and nuts in it. You add some milk to your cereal and sit down to eat while trying to remember all the things you need for school. As you get up, you accidentally knock over a copper salt shaker and some table salt spills out. You quickly clean up the mess with a sponge and water.

Next, it's off to the bathroom to brush your teeth. You love the feel of a clean mouth—baking soda toothpaste and minty mouthwash does the trick! Then, you jump into the shower and scrub yourself down with a bar of soap. You quickly get dressed and put on your silver necklace and gold earrings. Next, you're off to the kitchen to make your lunch for school. You pack two slices of leftover pepperoni pizza, a fruit salad, and a can of pop. You grab your backpack and head out the door. As you leave your house, you take a deep breath of fresh air and then exhale a cloud of carbon dioxide. Off to school you go.

1. **Marking the Text**

   Pure substances and mixtures are all around us. Using two different colours, highlight all the pure substances and mixtures mentioned in the reading passage.

2. **Comparing and Contrasting—Using Graphic Organizers**

   Comparing and contrasting helps us understand how two concepts are similar and different. Complete the Venn diagram to visually show the similarities and differences between an element and a compound.

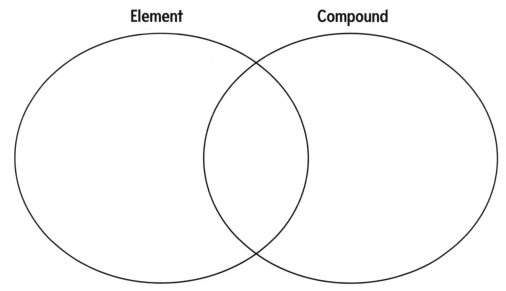

Element   Compound

3. Identifying Concepts

In the table below, compile a list of all the pure substances and mixtures that are mentioned in the reading passage in the order that they appear. Determine whether the sample is an **element**, a **compound**, a **homogeneous mixture** or a **heterogeneous mixture**. If the sample is a mixture, identify at least two substances that make up that mixture.

	Sample	Type of Matter	Substances in Mixture
a)			
b)			
c)			
d)			
e)			
f)			
g)			
h)			
i)			
j)			
k)			
l)			
m)			
n)			
o)			
p)			
q)			

Physical and Chemical Properties

Use with textbook pages 88–90.

Identify the physical or chemical property that is described in each statement.

1. Salt dissolves in water. _____

2. Copper produces a green flame. _____

3. An ice cube turns into water at 0 °C. _____

4. Sandpaper feels rough and gritty to the touch. _____

5. Dry Christmas trees can catch fire and burn easily. _____

6. The handle of a metal frying pan is too hot to touch. _____

7. Water heated in a kettle will turn to steam at 100 °C. _____

8. A spoonful of honey will pour slower than a spoonful of vegetable oil.

   _____

9. Gold is very soft and can be hammered into thin sheets to make jewellery.

   _____

10. Bubbles form and a gas is given off when vinegar is added to baking soda.

    _____

11. A copper penny becomes dull brown over time and eventually turns to dull light green.

    _____

12. Most elements can exist as a solid, a liquid, and a gas, depending on the temperature and pressure.

    _____

13. The strong triple bond between the atoms of a nitrogen molecule is the reason why nitrogen gas is unreactive.

    _____

Observing Chemical Reactions

Use with textbook pages 88-90.

Identify a visible sign that a chemical reaction has occurred in each description below.

1. A candle burns.

_____

2. A leftover sandwich starts to rot and smell.

_____

3. Potassium is added to a beaker of water and a flame appears.

_____

4. Exploding fireworks produce an array of beautiful colours and loud sounds.

_____

5. Wood is placed in a campfire. It starts to burn, and smoke and black ashes form.

_____

6. An iron chain left outside in the rain starts to rust, resulting in a reddish-brown colour.

_____

7. A piece of calcium metal is placed in a beaker of water. Bubbles of hydrogen gas form in the water.

_____

8. Colourless hydrochloric acid is poured into a beaker with a red solution of cobalt(II) nitrate. The solution turns blue.

_____

9. Dough is wrapped around a stick and roasted over an open fire. The bannock turns brown and is cooked all the way through.

_____

10. A solution of clear reddish-orange sodium dichromate is added to a colourless solution of lead nitrate. A yellow insoluble solid forms.

_____

Safety First

Use with textbook pages 91–93.

Use the following diagram to complete the table below.

1. Describe the potential safety hazard associated with each of the safety icons shown. Explain the precaution that the student should take for each safety hazard.

	Safety Icon		Safety Hazard	Precaution
a)	Eye Safety			
b)	Clothing Protection			
c)	Thermal Safety			
d)	Skin Protection			
e)	Electrical			
f)	Chemical Safety			

2.1 Assessment

Match each description on the left with the best safety icon on the right. Each safety icon may be used only once.

Description	Safety Icon
1. _____ wear safety goggles to protect your eyes	A.
2. _____ be careful when using electrical equipment	B.
3. _____ be careful when working around open flames	C.
4. _____ be careful when handling hot objects and glassware	D.
5. _____ wear a lab apron to protect clothing and skin from spills	E.
6. _____ wear gloves to protect the skin from corrosive chemicals	F.
7. _____ be careful when working with sharp objects that can cause cuts	G.
8. _____ be careful when handling chemicals that can cause burns or are poisonous when they come in contact with skin	H.

Circle the letter of the best answer for questions 9 to 26.

9. Which of the following is made up of one type of particle?

   A. tea

   B. lead

   C. granite

   D. garden salad

10. Which of the following consists of two or more pure substances?

   A. ice

   B. oxygen

   C. soda pop

   D. ammonia

11. Classify matter by identifying the type of pure substances and mixtures shown below.

	W	X	Y	Z
A.	element	homogeneous mixture	compound	heterogeneous mixture
B.	compound	homogeneous mixture	heterogeneous mixture	element
C.	compound	heterogeneous mixture	element	homogeneous mixture
D.	element	heterogeneous mixture	compound	homogeneous mixture

12. Which of the following is correctly paired?

    A. element – air

    B. compound – baking soda

    C. heterogeneous mixture – perfume

    D. homogeneous mixture – pulpy orange juice

13. Which of the following is a mixture that has the same composition throughout?

    A. gravel   **C.** granola cereal

    B. wet sand   **D.** stainless steel spoon

14. Which of the following can be separated by physical means?

    A. platinum   **C.** apple juice

    B. salt water   **D.** iron filings and sand mixture

15. Boiling can be used to separate the parts of which of the following mixtures?

    A. salt water

    B. fruit smoothie

    C. liquid mercury

    D. marble and sand mixture

16. Solid tin becomes a liquid at 232 °C. Liquid tin becomes a gas at 2603 °C. What physical properties of tin are described?

A. malleability and hardness

B. state of matter and solubility

C. melting point and boiling point

D. texture and ability to conduct heat and electricity

17. Which of the following statements uses viscosity and texture to describe the substance?

A. Maple syrup flows slowly and is very smooth.

B. Bromine is a reddish brown liquid at room temperature.

C. Aluminum is shiny and can be hammered into thin sheets.

D. Copper is a soft metal that will allow electric currents to flow through it.

18. Sugar can dissolve in water. What physical property is described?

A. solubility   **C.** hardness

B. viscosity   **D.** malleability

19. Gasoline vapour is highly flammable and can burn easily. What chemical property is described?

A. combustibility   **C.** reactivity with acids

B. lack of reactivity   **D.** reactivity with oxygen

20. A colourless solution of calcium nitrate is added to a colourless solution of sodium carbonate. A white precipitate is formed. How do you know a chemical reaction has occurred?

A. bubbles are formed   **C.** a gas is released

B. heat is given off   **D.** a new substance is formed

21. Concentrated sulfuric acid is added to a sugar solution. Bubbles form as a result. Which of the following explains the presence of the bubbles?

A. a gas was formed

B. there was a colour change in the solution

C. smoke from the thermal energy was released

D. heat was produced in the chemical reaction

22. Which of the following is a safe practice in the science lab?

  A. tie back long hair

  B. remove the electrical plug from the socket by pulling on the cord

  C. place the container directly under your nose and inhale the fumes

  D. dispose of leftover chemicals by pouring them back into the original container

23. An investigation requires you to pour some hydrochloric acid into a test tube. Which of the following describes why it is important to wear gloves when working with corrosive chemicals?

  A. to prevent contact with your skin

  B. to have a better grip on the test tube

  C. to protect the hydrochloric acid from contamination

  D. to prevent the heat from your hands from reacting with the hydrochloric acid

24. You accidentally spilled some sodium hydroxide on your arm during an investigation. Which of the following is the best procedure to deal with this situation?

  A. wash your arm thoroughly with cold water

  B. remove the chemical by rubbing it vigorously with a piece of paper towel

  C. let the sodium hydroxide dry and see if your skin is irritated by the chemical

  D. leave it alone because sodium hydroxide will evaporate off the surface of your skin

25. When would you see the following safety icon in a science investigation?

  A. when you are working with open flames

  B. when you are using a razor blade during a dissection

  C. when you need to take care with the disposal of blood from your finger

  D. when you are working with chemicals that can produce dangerous fumes

26. Which of the following describes the proper way to clean up after an investigation?

    A. leave the laboratory burner on for the next class

    B. pour all the chemicals used in the lab down the sink

    C. clean up any chemical spills as directed by your teacher

    D. leave any electrical equipment plugged in for the next class

27. Complete the following Frayer model diagram for a pure substance.

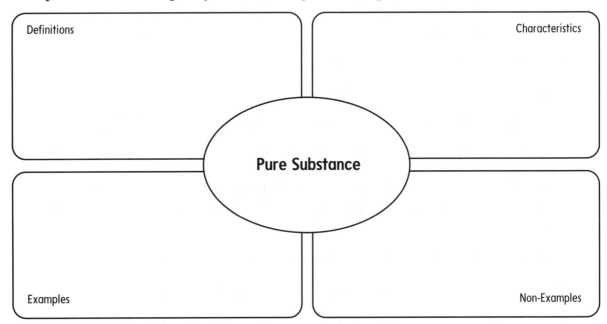

Definitions   Characteristics

Pure Substance

Examples   Non-Examples

28. Complete the following Frayer model diagram for a mixture.

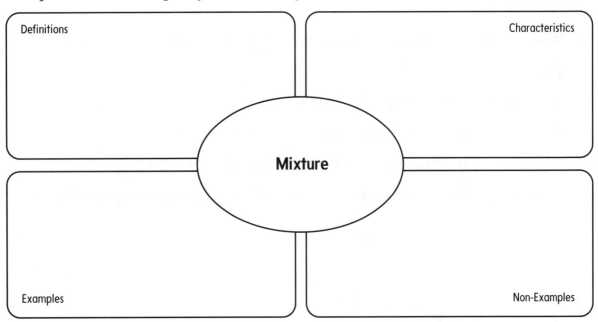

Definitions   Characteristics

Mixture

Examples   Non-Examples

How does the periodic table organize the elements?

Use with textbook pages 100–115.

Element Names and Symbols

Each chemical element on the periodic table is given a unique symbol consisting of one or two letters. The first letter is always capitalized and if there is a second letter, it is always lowercase. The chemical names for many of the elements come from ancient languages like Latin and Greek. Others are named after countries or famous scientists.

Dmitri Mendeleev

Dmitri Mendeleev created a chart that is now known as the periodic table. He organized the known elements at the time into columns (groups or families) and rows (periods) based on their chemical and physical properties, but left gaps in his arrangements. These gaps were later recognized as a powerful tool as they predicted the existence of elements not yet discovered.

Periodic Table

The periodic table separates the elements into three categories based on their chemical and physical properties: metals, non-metals, and semi-metals. Groups 1, 2, and 13 to 18 are known as main-group elements. Groups 3 to 12 are called transition elements. The inner transition metals are shown in two rows at the bottom of the table to keep the table compact.

Metals

The **metals** are located to the left of the zigzag line on the periodic table. They are shiny, malleable, ductile, and good conductors of thermal energy and electric current. The **alkali metals (Group 1)** are the most reactive metals and will react readily with other substances. The **alkaline-earth metals (Group 2)** are also highly reactive, but are not as reactive as the alkali metals.

Non-metals

The **non-metals** are found to the right of the zigzag line. They are generally gases or brittle, dull-looking solids that are poor conductors of heat and electrical current. **Halogens (Group 17)** are the most reactive non-metals. **Hydrogen** is a non-metal that is colourless, odourless, but highly flammable. The **noble gases (Group 18)** are stable elements and are the least reactive of all the elements.

Semi-metals

Semi-metals or metalloids are found along the zigzag line. They have properties of both metals and non-metals. They are shiny like metals, but are brittle and not ductile like non-metals. They are poor conductors of thermal energy and electric current.

The Origin of Element Names and Symbols

Use with textbook pages 100–103, 106.

Many elements have a Latin or Greek origin. Some are named after scientists who have made contributions to science. Others come from countries or continents. Use the Periodic Table of the Elements to determine the element and chemical symbol from the clues given.

	Element	Symbol	Latin Origin
1.			Calx – Latin for "limestone"
2.			Caesius – Latin for "bluish grey"
3.			Aurum – Latin for "gold"
4.			Ferrum – Latin for "iron"
5.			Plumbum – Latin for "lead"
6.			Rubidus – Latin for "red"
7.			Argentum – Latin for "silver"
8.			Stannum – Latin for "tin"

	Element	Symbol	Greek Origin
9.			Argon – Greek for "inactive"
10.			Bromos – Greek for "smelly stench"
11.			Chloros – Greek for "yellowish green"
12.			Iodes – Greek for "violet"

	Element	Symbol	Scientist the Element was Named After
13.			Niels Bohr (contributed to atomic theory)
14.			Marie and Pierre Curie (discovered radium)
15.			Dmitri Mendeleev (invented the periodic table)
16.			Rutherford (contributed to atomic theory)

	Element	Symbol	Place the Element was Named After
17.			America
18.			France
19.			Germany
20.			Poland

The Predictive Power of the Periodic Table

Use with textbook pages 104–105.

Use the following diagram representing Mendeleev's periodic table to answer questions 1 to 9.

I										
H 1.01	II	III	IV	V	VI	VII				
Li 6.94	Be 9.01	B 10.81	C 12.01	N 14.01	O 16.00	F 19.00				
Na 22.99	Mg 24.31	Al 26.98	Si 28.09	P 30.97	S 32.07	Cl 35.45	VIII			
K 39.10	Ca 40.08		Ti 47.87	V 50.94	Cr 52.00	Mn 54.94	Fe 55.85	Co 58.93	Ni 58.69	
Cu 63.55	Zn 65.41			As 74.92	Se 78.96	Br 79.90				
Rb 85.47	Sr 87.62	Y 88.91	Zr 91.22	Nb 92.91	Mo 95.94		Ru 101.07	Rh 102.91	Pd 106.42	
Ag 107.87	Cd 112.41	In 114.32	Sn 118.71	Sb 121.76	Te 127.60	I 126.90				
Ce 140.12	Ba 137.33	La 138.91		Ta 180.95	W 183.84		Os 190.23	Ir 192.22	Pt 195.08	
Au 196.97	Hg 200.59	Tl 204.38	Pb 207.2	Bi 208.98						
			Th 232.04	U 238.03						

1. Why do think it is fitting for this tabular arrangement to be called a "periodic" table?

_____

2. Mendeleev noticed trends and used columns and rows to organize the known elements. From the table above, what can you infer about how Mendeleev arranged the elements?

_____

3. What do you think the white gaps in Mendeleev's periodic table represent?

_____

4. Mendeleev's decision to leave these gaps made his periodic table successful. What made Mendeleev certain that he should leave gaps in his table?

_____

5. Analyze Mendeleev's periodic table. Describe the predictive power of his tabular arrangement.

_____

6. Can you predict the atomic mass of the unknown element that is located between Mo and Ru? Explain your answer.

_____

7. Would you expect to see the unknown element that is between La and Ta to have the same properties as Ti and Zr? Explain.

_____

8. Mendeleev placed "I" and "Te" out of order, even though "I" had a lower relative atomic mass than "Te." Explain why you think he switched these adjacent elements.

_____

9. Mendeleev accurately predicted the existence of unknown elements that have the same properties as the other elements in the same column. He was able to figure out their atomic mass and predict their properties using his periodic table. The diagram below shows Mendeleev's prediction of an element which he called eka-boron.

Mendeleev's Table

Property of eka-boron

Property	Mendeleev's Prediction	Actual Data
Atomic mass	44	43.79
Density (g/cm³)	3.5	3.86
Solubility of oxide	dissolves in acid	dissolves in acid

a) Based on Mendeleev's periodic table, eka-boron is located between which two elements?

_____

b) How was Mendeleev able to predict that eka-boron has a density of 3.5 g/cm^3 and that it dissolves in acid?

_____

c) Which elements would you expect eka-boron to have the same properties as?

_____

d) What is the current accepted element name for eka-boron?

_____

The Modern Periodic Table

Use with textbook pages 106–109.

Use the diagram to answer questions 1 to 4.

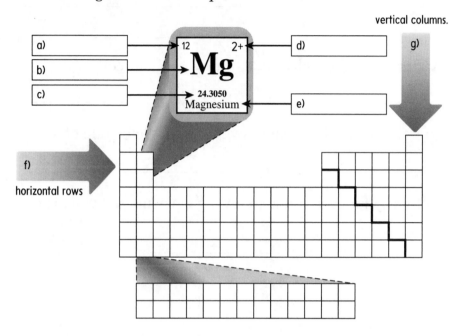

1. Label the five different parts of a typical box from the periodic table and label the two arrows shown.

2. Describe what each labelled part represents.

    a) _____

    b) _____

    c) _____

    d) _____

    e) _____

    f) _____

    g) _____

3. The modern periodic table has the same basic structure as Mendeleev's original periodic table, but with a slight change based on Moseley's contribution.

    a) What fundamental characteristic is now used to characterize and arrange elements in the modern periodic table?

    _____

b) How does this new organizing scheme resolve problems that Mendeleev encountered with the reordering of adjacent elements like tellurium and iodine or cobalt and nickel?

_____

_____

4. List two ways in which elements are logically organized in a meaningful way.

_____

5. As you move from left to right along a horizontal row, what trend do you notice?

_____

6. Examine the periodic table entry for each of the following elements and complete the blanks.

a)

20	2+
Ca	
Calcium	
40.1	

i. atomic number _____

ii. average atomic mass _____

iii. ion charge _____

iv. symbol for element _____

b)

17	–
Cl	
Chlorine	
35.5	

i. name of element _____

ii. ion charge _____

iii. average atomic mass _____

iv. number of protons _____

c)

13	3+
Al	
Aluminum	
27.0	

i. name of element _____

ii. number of protons _____

iii. ion charge _____

iv. symbol for element _____

d)

34	2–
Se	
Selenium	
79.0	

i. atomic number _____

ii. name of element _____

iii. ion charge _____

iv. symbol for element _____

Metals, Non-metals, and Semi-metals

Use with textbook pages 110–114.

1. Identifying the Main Ideas and Details

To identify the main ideas in Concept 4 of Topic 2.2, use the following strategies:

- pay attention to headings and subheadings
- skim the text and figures to have a visual overview of the content
- note the terms that are boldfaced and italicized

a) What are the three headings and subheadings covered in Concept 4? Be sure to consider information found in figures and tables.

_____

_____

_____

_____

b) List the terms that are boldfaced and italicized.

_____

_____

_____

_____

2. Monitoring Comprehension

As you read, stop after each paragraph to check your understanding. Place a small sticky note beside each paragraph. Put a ✓ if you comprehend the concepts covered and put an ✗ if you do not understand or are confused about the content. For the paragraph that you *do* understand, rephrase the main ideas in your own words. For the paragraph that you *do not* understand, use the following strategies:

- reread the paragraph
- identify the part that is confusing you or that you do not understand
- if a key term is unclear, look up its definition in the glossary
- if a concept is unclear or confusing, look for visuals on the page to help you understand the concept

3. Making Study Notes

Now that you have identified headings, subheadings, and key terms, make study notes to help you reinforce main ideas by putting them in your own words. Read each paragraph and write point-form notes using these strategies:

- change each heading and subheading into a question
- list details that answer the question
- include the key terms that are boldfaced or italicized and give their definitions
- include examples

4. Comparing and Contrasting—Using Graphic Organizers

Comparing and contrasting using a Venn diagram helps you see how metals, non-metals, and semi-metals are similar to and different from each other. Place the letter of each description in the appropriate place in the Venn diagram.

A. brittle

B. ductile

C. not shiny

D. malleable

E. not ductile

F. not malleable

G. shiny and smooth

H. dull-looking solids

I. includes halogens

J. includes noble gases

K. includes alkali metals

L. gases at room temperature

M. includes alkaline-earth metals

N. mostly solids at room temperature

O. poor conductors of electric current

P. poor conductors of thermal energy

Q. good conductors of electric current

R. good conductors of thermal energy

S. some elements are liquids at room temperature

T. has an atomic mass and a distinct atomic number

U. have physical and chemical properties of both metals and non-metals

V. can react with other elements to form compounds (except most noble gases)

W. elements that are made of atoms consisting of protons, electrons and neutrons

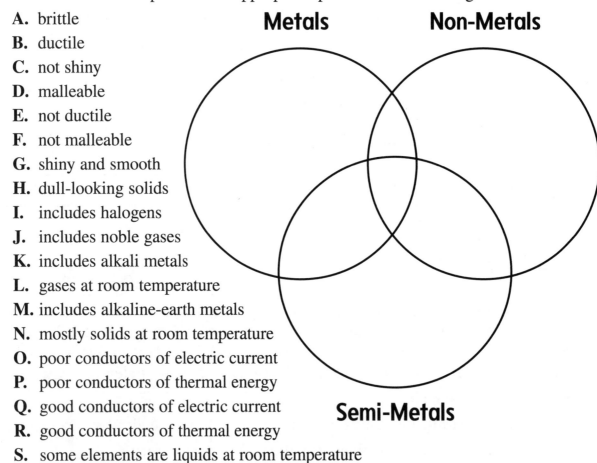

Metals   Non-Metals

Semi-Metals

Comparing Alkali Metals to Alkaline-Earth Metals

Use with textbook pages 110–114.

1. Compare and contrast alkali metals to alkaline-earth metals by completing the graphic organizer.

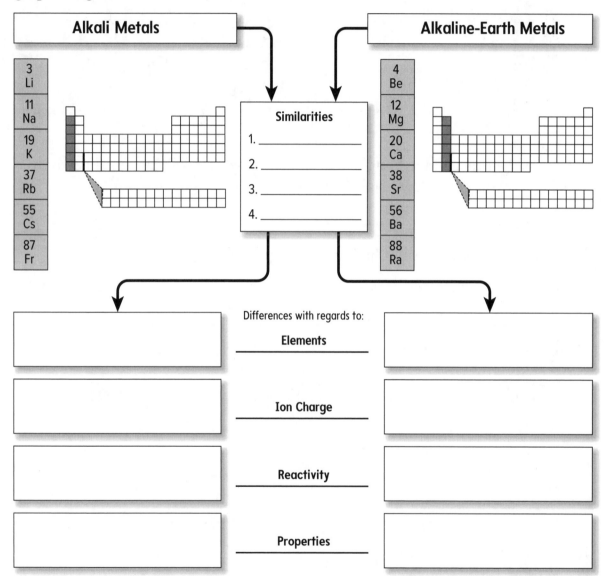

2. Compared to sodium, is magnesium more or less reactive?

_____

3. Name three physical properties that lithium and beryllium have in common.

_____

Use the following graphs showing melting points to answer questions 4 to 6.

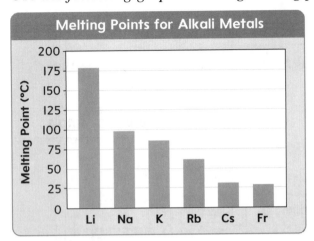

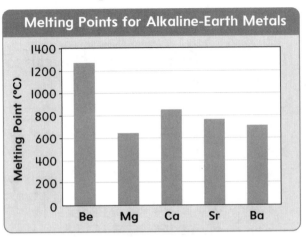

4. How is the change in melting points similar between alkali and alkaline-earth metals as you move down both groups?

_____

5. Which group of metals has higher melting points? _____

6. Analyze both graphs. What are the states of these metals at room temperature?

_____

Use the following tables to answer questions 7 to 9.

Group 1 (Alkali Metals)	Density (g/cm³)
Lithium	0.53
Sodium	0.97
Potassium	0.86
Rubidium	1.53
Cesium	1.88

Group 2 (Alkaline-Earth Metals)	Density (g/cm³)
Beryllium	1.85
Magnesium	1.74
Calcium	1.54
Strontium	2.54
Barium	3.51

7. Describe the trend in density as you move down Group 1 and Group 2.

_____

8. How do alkali metals and alkaline-earth metals compare with respect to density?

_____

9. Would any of the alkaline-earth metals float on water (density: 1 g/cm³)? Explain how you know from the data given.

_____

2.2 Assessment

Match each term on the left with the best diagram of the periodic table on the right. Each section of the periodic table may be used only once.

Term	Diagram of the Periodic Table
1. ____ metals	A.
2. ____ halogens	B.
3. ____ non-metals	C.
4. ____ semi-metals	D.
5. ____ alkali metals	E.
6. ____ noble gases	F.
7. ____ alkaline-earth metals	G.

Circle the letter of the best answer for questions 8 to 20.

8. If a new element, venusium, is discovered, which of the following could be its possible chemical symbol?

A. ve

B. Ve

C. VE

D. VeN

9. Which of the following elements is the most reactive?

A. helium

B. rubidium

C. magnesium

D. phosphorus

10. Which of the following elements are liquids at room temperature?

I	Bromine
II	Mercury
III	Chlorine

A. I and II only

B. I and III only

C. II and III only

D. I, II, and III

11. What do potassium, beryllium, and nickel all have in common?

I	They are solids at room temperature.
II	They are shiny, ductile, and malleable.
III	They are good conductors of heat and electricity.

A. I and II only

B. I and III only

C. II and III only

D. I, II, and III

12. An unknown element is a shiny, non-ductile solid, and is a poor conductor of thermal energy. This unknown element would be classified as

A. a metal.

B. a non-metal.

C. a semi-metal.

D. an inner transition metal.

13. Element "X" is a gas at room temperature and is highly reactive. In which group would element "X" most likely belong?

A. the halogens

B. the noble gases

C. the alkali metals

D. the alkaline-earth metals

14. Which of the following pairs of elements would have similar properties?

    A. boron and carbon

    B. strontium and iodine

    C. phosphorus and argon

    D. germanium and arsenic

15. Which two elements belong to the same group?

    A. aluminum and silicon

    B. hydrogen and helium

    C. lithium and beryllium

    D. oxygen and selenium

16. Which two elements belong to the same period?

    A. helium and xenon

    B. cerium and thorium

    C. sodium and scandium

    D. rubidium and antimony

17. Which of the following is unique to each element on the periodic table?

I	its chemical symbol
II	the group or family it belongs to
III	the number of protons in the atom

    A. I and II only

    B. I and III only

    C. II and III only

    D. I, II, and III

Use the following graph showing the melting and boiling points of alkali metals to answer questions 18 and 19.

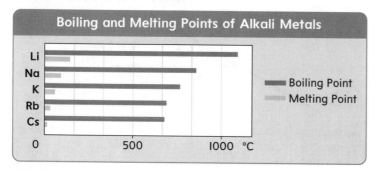

18. Both melting and boiling points decrease as you move down Group 1, from lithium to cesium.

    A. This statement is supported by the graph.

    B. This statement is refuted by the graph.

    C. This statement is neither supported nor refuted by the graph.

19. The melting points are at higher temperatures than the boiling points.

   A. This statement is supported by the graph.

   B. This statement is refuted by the graph.

   C. This statement is neither supported nor refuted by the graph.

Use the following graph showing the density of the noble gases to answer question 20.

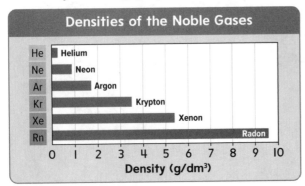

20. Which of the following statements are true about the densities of the noble gases?

I	Argon is more dense than krypton.
II	Xenon is about five times denser than neon.
III	There is an increase in density going down Group 18, from helium to radon.

   A. I and II only

   B. I and III only

   C. II and III only

   D. I, II, and III

21. Complete a spider map for the four major families on the periodic table.

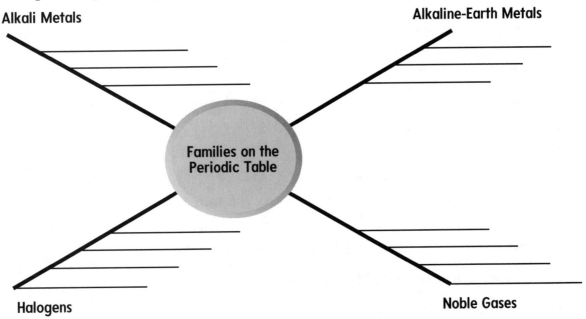

How can atomic theory explain patterns in the periodic table?

Use with textbook pages 122–133.

Parts of the Atom

The **atom** is the smallest particle of an element. It consists of three **subatomic particles**: protons, electrons, and neutrons. **Protons** (p^+) are positively charged particles, while **neutrons** (n^0) are particles with no charge. Both protons and neutrons are found in the dense, positively charged centre of the atom called the **nucleus**. The nucleus accounts for most of the atom's mass. **Electrons** (e^-) are negatively charged particles that exist in specific **energy** shells around the nucleus. Refer to Figure 2.15 and Table 2.3 on page 124 in the textbook to see a summary of the parts of an atom.

Bohr Diagrams

A **Bohr diagram** shows the electron arrangements of atoms and ions. The first energy shell can hold a maximum of two electrons, while the second and third energy shells can hold a maximum of eight electrons. The outermost energy shell of an atom is called the **valence shell**, and the electrons occupying this shell are called **valence electrons**. The diagram below shows the two different ways to draw a Bohr diagram.

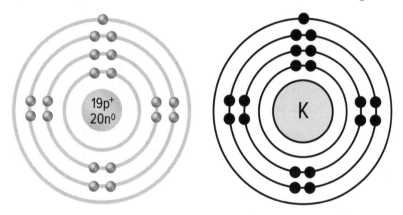

Elements in the Same Groups and Periods

Elements that belong to the *same group* (vertical column) have the same number of valence electrons. For example, beryllium and magnesium belong to Group 2 and so they both have two valence electrons. Elements that belong to the *same period* (horizontal row) have the same number of energy shells. For example, sodium and sulfur both belong to Period 3 and therefore have three occupied energy shells. Analyze Figure 2.17 on page 126 of the textbook. How is the electron configuration similar for elements from the same group and period?

Full Valence Shells

Noble gases are the only elements on the periodic table that have
full valence shells. This is what makes them stable. Atoms can obtain
full valence shells like the noble gases, by forming ions. Ions are charged particles that
have gained or lost electrons. Metals tend to lose electrons and non-metals tend to gain
electrons to become stable ions with full valence shells. The figure below shows how an
atom can give up an electron or gain an electron to become an ion.

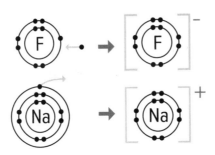

Periodic Trend

Periodic trend refers to the regular pattern in the properties of elements on the periodic
table. These trends help us predict the properties of an element. There are two clear
trends.

1. Atomic size

The atomic size increases moving down a group. For example, in the alkali metals,
potassium (in Period 4) is larger than lithium (in Period 2) because it has more occupied
energy shells and its valence electrons are farther away from the nucleus.

The atomic size decreases going from left to right across a period. For example, in
Period 2, lithium (in the first column) is larger than neon (in the last column). Neon has
10 protons, while lithium has 3 protons. So, the positively charged protons exert a
greater pull on the negatively charged electrons, bringing them closer to the nucleus.

2. Reactivity

The reactivity of metals increases moving down a group. For example, rubidium (in
Period 5) is much more reactive in water than lithium (in Period 2) is for the alkali
metals. As you move down a group, the atoms get bigger. So, valence electrons are
farther from the nucleus, and there is less pull on them.

Parts of the Atom

Use with textbook page 124.

1. Check Your Understanding

As you read the paragraph on Key Features of Atomic Structure on page 124 of the textbook, stop and reread any parts that you do not understand. Write down any sentences that help you understand the concepts better.

2. Summarizing

Summarizing means to restate the main ideas in your own words. A summary can be in point form or in sentence form. Read the paragraph on Key Features of Atomic Structure on page 124 of the textbook. Complete the following table by using point form to summarize the main ideas in the textbook paragraph. Write a summary sentence. Compare your table and points with a partner.

Section of the Textbook	Main Topic	What the Text Says About the Main Topic	Supporting Details
Page 124, "Key Features of Atomic Structure"			

Summary Sentence: _____

_____

3. Interpreting Tables

A table organizes information in rows and columns so that it can visually display concepts in an organized way for the reader. Refer to Table 2.3 on page 124 in the textbook. In Table 2.3, the word *nucleus* appears in the second row of the last column. The information can be interpreted as "Protons are located in the nucleus of an atom."

a) Analyze Table 2.3. Cover the table and read the boldfaced titles of each column. Based on the title, explain what you would expect to the see in the cells below it.

_____

_____

b) Choose a cell in Table 2.3. Interpret the contents of the cell by writing a complete sentence.

_____

_____

4. Interpreting Diagrams

A diagram is a visual representation of some text that uses words and symbols to represent an object. Determine how each part of the diagram shows the main ideas in the paragraph and Table 2.3 from the textbook.

In the numbered boxes, identify the parts of an atom using the following terms: **electron**, **energy shell**, **neutron**, **nucleus**, **proton**. Describe the characteristics of the different parts of the atom by completing the boxes.

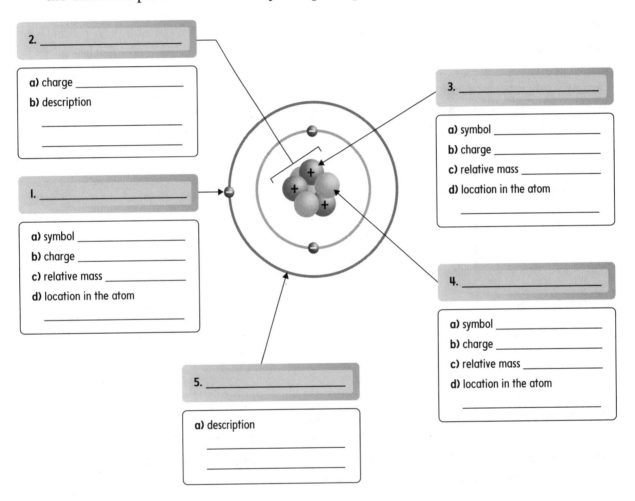

2. _____

a) charge _____
b) description
_____
_____

1. _____

a) symbol _____
b) charge _____
c) relative mass _____
d) location in the atom
_____

3. _____

a) symbol _____
b) charge _____
c) relative mass _____
d) location in the atom
_____

4. _____

a) symbol _____
b) charge _____
c) relative mass _____
d) location in the atom
_____

5. _____

a) description
_____
_____

Bohr Diagrams

Use with textbook page 125.

1. Define the following terms.

    a) Bohr diagram _____

    b) valence shell _____

    c) valence electron _____

2. List two things that a Bohr diagram shows.

    a) _____

    b) _____

3. What is the maximum number of electrons that can be found in

    a) the first energy shell? _____

    b) the second energy shell? _____

    c) the third energy shell? _____

4. Draw the Bohr diagram for each of the following atoms.

a) lithium	b) magnesium	c) aluminum
d) oxygen	**e) chlorine**	**f) argon**

Full Valence Shells

Use with textbook page 127.

1. What information does the charge of an ion give?

   _____

2. Why do atoms become ions? _____

3. **a)** Draw the Bohr diagram for a fluoride ion and a sodium ion in the first two
   columns of the table.

Fluorine Ion	Sodium Ion	Noble Gas = _____

   b) What noble gas would have the same electron arrangement as a fluorine ion and
   a sodium ion? Draw the Bohr diagram for that noble gas in the third column of
   the table above.

   c) What do these two ions have in common with the noble gas?

   _____

4. **a)** Draw the Bohr diagram for a helium atom in the first column of the table.

Helium Atom	Ion #1 = _____	Ion #2 = _____

   b) What two ions would have the same electron arrangement as a helium atom?
   Draw the Bohr diagrams for these two ions in the second and third columns in
   the table above.

Electron Arrangements Show Patterns

Use with textbook page 126.

1. Consider the electron arrangements of nitrogen, oxygen, and fluorine.

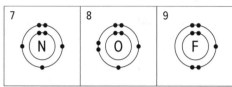

a) What do all three of these elements have in common with respect to their position on the periodic table?

_____

b) How is the number of occupied energy shells related to the period?

_____

2. Consider the electron arrangements of beryllium and magnesium.

a) What do elements in Group 2 have in common?

_____

b) How does this relate to their group number?

_____

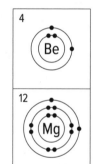

3. a) Which family on the periodic table has full valence shells?

_____

b) How is the electron arrangement in helium different from the other noble gases?

_____

4. Consider the six elements shown.

 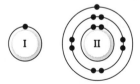   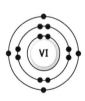

a) Which of these elements belong to the same group?

_____

b) Which of these elements belong to the same period?

_____

Periodic Trends

Use with textbook pages 130–131.

Use the following graphs showing the atomic radii for elements in Group 1 and Group 2 to answer questions 1 to 4.

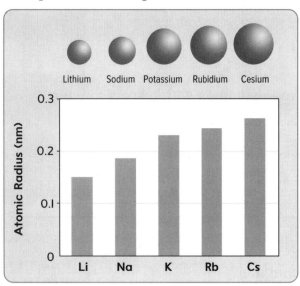

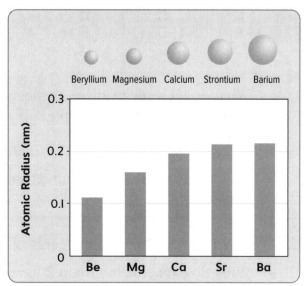

1. What happens to the atomic size as you move down the two groups of elements shown above?

   _____

2. Predict the trend in the atomic size as you move down the halogen group.

   _____

3. Comparing adjacent elements on the same period (e.g., cesium and barium), which metal group has the bigger atomic size?

   _____

4. Why do you think calcium is almost twice as big as beryllium?

   _____

   _____

   _____

Use the diagram on reactivity to answer questions 5 to 8.

5. a) Between lithium, sodium, and potassium, which of these three alkali metals is the most reactive? Explain your answer.

_____

_____

_____

_____

b) What does this suggest about the reactivity of alkali metals as you move down the group on the periodic table?

_____

_____

6. Noting the periodic trend, predict whether rubidium would react more or less vigorously in water than potassium. Explain your answer.

_____

_____

_____

7. Note the relative reactivity of sodium and magnesium. What happens to the reactivity of metals as you move from left to right across the same period?

_____

_____

8. Noting the periodic trend, predict whether lithium or beryllium would be more reactive. Explain your answer.

_____

_____

_____

Increasing Reactivity

Potassium

Sodium

Lithium

Calcium

Magnesium

Aluminum

Zinc

Iron

Copper

Silver

Gold

2.3 Assessment

Match each term on the left with the best description on the right. Each descriptor may be used only once.

Term	Description
1. ____ ion	A. the outermost energy shell of an atom
2. ____ atom	B. the electrons in the outermost energy shell of an atom
3. ____ valence shell	C. protons, electrons, and neutrons that make up an atom
4. ____ Bohr diagram	D. a particle that has equal numbers of protons and electrons
5. ____ periodic trends	E. a particle that has a charge because it has lost or gained electrons
6. ____ valence electrons	F. a drawing that shows the electron arrangements in individual energy shells
7. ____ subatomic particles	G. regular patterns seen in the properties of elements due to their atomic structure

Circle the letter of the best answer for questions 8 to 21.

8. Which subatomic particles are found in the nucleus of an atom?

A. protons and neutrons

B. protons and electrons

C. electrons and neutrons

D. electrons, protons, and neutrons

9. Which of the following describes the difference between a magnesium atom and a magnesium ion?

A. A magnesium atom has more protons than a magnesium ion.

B. A magnesium ion has more neutrons than a magnesium atom.

C. A magnesium atom has more electrons than a magnesium ion.

D. A magnesium atom has a positive charge and a magnesium ion has no charge.

10. Which of the following shows how a chlorine atom compares to a chloride ion?

	Chlorine Atom	Chloride Ion
A.	17 protons, 17 electrons	17 protons, 17 electrons
B.	17 protons, 17 electrons	17 protons, 18 electrons
C.	17 protons, 18 electrons	17 protons, 17 electrons
D.	17 protons, 18 electrons	17 protons, 18 electrons

Use the following Bohr diagram to answer questions 11 to 15.

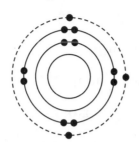

11. Which element is represented by the Bohr diagram?

    A. a silicon atom

    B. an aluminum atom

    C. a magnesium atom

    D. a phosphorus atom

12. To what period does this atom belong?

    A. Period 1

    B. Period 2

    C. Period 3

    D. Period 4

13. How does this atom acquire a full valence shell?

    A. by losing 3 protons

    B. by gaining 3 protons

    C. by losing 3 electrons

    D. by gaining 3 electrons

14. When this atom becomes an ion, what is its ion charge?

    A. 2–

    B. 2+

    C. 3–

    D. 3+

15. What noble gas has the same electron arrangement as the ion for this element?

    A. helium

    B. neon

    C. argon

    D. krypton

16. How many valence electrons does a phosphorus atom have?

    A. 2

    B. 3

    C. 4

    D. 5

17. How many energy shells do a magnesium atom, a silicon atom, and a chlorine atom each have?

    A. 1

    B. 2

    C. 3

    D. 4

18. Which of the following particles have the same electron arrangements?

   A. a lithium ion, a sodium ion, and a helium atom

   B. a fluoride atom, a sodium ion, and a neon atom

   C. a magnesium ion, a fluoride ion, and a neon atom

   D. a chloride ion, a potassium atom, and an argon atom

19. Amongst the halogens, which correctly compares the relative size of the atoms?

   A. iodine is larger than astatine

   B. chlorine is larger than iodine

   C. astatine is larger than fluorine

   D. fluorine is larger than chlorine

20. Rank the following elements from largest to smallest: calcium, bromine, potassium.

	Largest ⟶		Smallest
A.	bromine	calcium	potassium
B.	calcium	potassium	bromine
C.	potassium	bromine	calcium
D.	potassium	calcium	bromine

21. Which of the following elements is more reactive than chlorine?

   A. sulfur   C. fluorine

   B. argon   D. bromine

22. Complete a KWL chart for periodic trend.

K What I Know	W What I Want to Know	L What I Learned

How do elements combine to form compounds?

Use with textbook pages 136–151.

Ionic Compounds

An **ionic compound** consists of a positively charged ion and a negatively charged ion, held together by strong **ionic bonds**. A *binary ionic compound* is made up of two elements: a metal transfers its electron(s) to a non-metal, so that full valence shells can be achieved. The diagram below shows how a sodium atom transfers its electron to the chlorine atom to form stable ions in the ionic compound, sodium chloride.

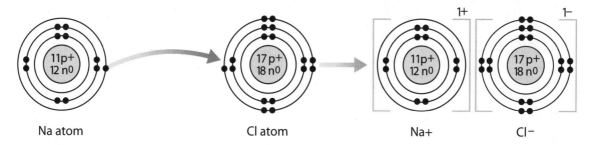

| Na atom | Cl atom | Na+ | Cl− |

The ions in ionic compounds form repeating patterns called lattices. Ionic compounds tend to have high melting points, are hard and brittle, conduct thermal energy, and conduct electric current when in liquid form or dissolved in a liquid such as water.

Covalent Compounds

A **covalent compound** consists of two or more non-metals held together by strong **covalent bonds**. These bonds are created when the elements share their valence electrons. Glucose, $C_6H_{12}O_6$, is an example of a covalent compound. A **molecule** is formed when two or more atoms are bonded together by covalent bonds. Water, H_2O, is an example of a molecule where hydrogen is bonded to oxygen by covalent bonds. Refer to Figure 2.29 on page 145 of the textbook to see three different models used to represent covalent compounds. The non-metals in covalent compounds can achieve stability of full valence shells by sharing their electrons. Analyze Table 2.4 on page 146. How can metals and non-metals achieve full valence shells?

In contrast to ionic compounds, covalent compounds have low melting points, are soft, and are poor conductors of electric current and thermal energy.

Diatomic Molecules

There are seven elements on the periodic table that exist as **diatomic molecules** in nature: H_2, O_2, F_2, Br_2, I_2, N_2, Cl_2. Note that they consist of two atoms that share electrons. Figure 2.33 on page 148 in the textbook shows how single bonds, double bonds, and triple bonds can form in diatomic molecules.

Elements and Compounds in the Human Body

Use with textbook pages 136–139.

Use the following information showing the elements that make up the human body to answer questions 1 to 10.

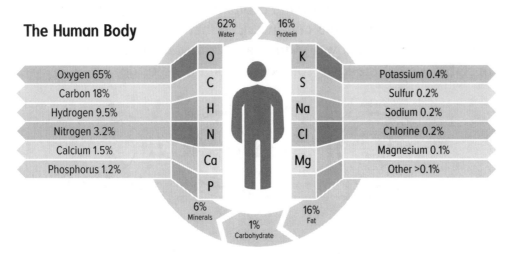

The Human Body

62% Water   16% Protein

Oxygen 65%
Carbon 18%
Hydrogen 9.5%
Nitrogen 3.2%
Calcium 1.5%
Phosphorus 1.2%

O
C
H
N
Ca
P

K
S
Na
Cl
Mg

Potassium 0.4%
Sulfur 0.2%
Sodium 0.2%
Chlorine 0.2%
Magnesium 0.1%
Other >0.1%

6% Minerals   1% Carbohydrate   16% Fat

1. Create a pie chart to display the percent by mass of the elements in the human body.

2. Why do you think a pie chart might be more useful than the diagram to visually display the information?

_____

_____

3. List the four elements that make up the majority of the human body mass.

_____

4. What percent of the human body do these four elements make up altogether?

_____

5. What do these four elements have in common?

_____

6. Which element is the most abundant in the human body?

_____

7. Why do you think there is a huge percent of oxygen and hydrogen in the human body?

_____

8. Proteins and fats make up about a third of the body. What elements do you think make up these two compounds?

_____

9. Do you think that every person will have the same percent of water, proteins, and fats in his/her body? What do you think these percents will depend on?

_____

10. What questions do you have about the essential elements that make up the body? Decide which questions you want to investigate. Develop a plan for how you want to investigate and research the answers to these questions.

_____

_____

_____

_____

_____

Electrical Conductivity of Ionic and Covalent Compounds

Use with textbook pages 140–147.

Use the following experimental set ups and conductivity graph to answer questions 1 to 15.

An experiment is carried out to test the conductivity of different solutions. The following table outlines the procedures carried out in the experiment.

Set Up #1 Distilled Water (H_2O)	Set Up #2 Sugar ($C_{12}H_{22}O_{11}$)	Set Up #3 Salt (NaCl)
Procedure: 1. Place 250 mL of distilled water in a beaker. 2. Connect two metal electrodes to a light bulb and put in the beaker with the water.	**Procedure:** 1. Place 10 g of sugar in a beaker with 250 mL of distilled water. Dissolve the sugar in the water. 2. Connect two metal electrodes to a light bulb and put in the beaker with the sugar solution.	**Procedure:** 1. Place 10 g of salt in a beaker with 250 mL of distilled water. Dissolve the salt in the water. 2. Connect two metal electrodes to a light bulb and put in the beaker with the salt solution.

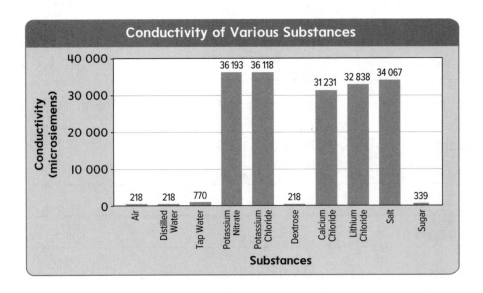

Conductivity of Various Substances

Conductivity (microsiemens) vs Substances

Air	Distilled Water	Tap Water	Potassium Nitrate	Potassium Chloride	Dextrose	Calcium Chloride	Lithium Chloride	Salt	Sugar
218	218	770	36 193	36 118	218	31 231	32 838	34 067	339

1. Define conductivity.

_____

2. What type of compound is salt (NaCl)? What bond holds the atoms in this compound together?

_____

3. What type of compound is sugar ($C_{12}H_{22}O_{11}$)? What bond holds the atoms together in this compound?

_____

4. What is the purpose of having a beaker of distilled water in this experiment?

_____

5. What happened to the salt when it dissolved in water?

_____

6. Which beaker(s) would you expect to have positively and negatively charged ions that are able to move freely?

_____

7. Which beaker(s) have uncharged particles in the solution?

_____

8. At the atomic level, what do you think the salt (NaCl) compounds and sugar ($C_{12}H_{22}O_{11}$) compounds look like before and after they are placed and dissolved in water? Draw some diagrams in the boxes below to show this.

Salt	Sugar
Salt **Before** It Dissolved in Water	Sugar **Before** It Dissolved in Water
Salt **After** It Dissolved in Water	Sugar **After** It Dissolved in Water

9. What do you think allows water to conduct electricity?

_____

10. According to the graph, which set up(s) will not conduct electricity and not light up the light bulb? Explain.

_____

_____

_____

11. According to the graph, which set up(s) will conduct electricity and light up the light bulb? Explain.

_____

_____

_____

12. Analyze the conductivity graph. What do all the compounds that are good conductors of electric current have in common?

_____

13. Based on its conductivity shown in the graph, predict whether dextrose is an ionic compound or a covalent compound. Explain your answer.

_____

14. Predict what would happen to the brightness of the light bulb if you added more salt to the solution in set up #3. Explain your reasoning.

_____

15. **a)** Reflect on your experiences with conductivity. What new questions do you have about conductivity? Come up with two questions about conductivity. State them in the form of testable questions.

_____

_____

b) Now state a hypothesis and a prediction based on your testable questions so that they can be answered through scientific investigations.

_____

_____

Properties of Ionic and Covalent Compounds

Use with textbook pages 140–147.

Use the following information to answer questions 1 to 10.

Compound	Formula	Melting Point (°C)	Boiling Point (°C)
sodium iodide	NaI	660	1304
calcium chloride	$CaCl_2$	782	1600
lithium bromide	LiBr	845	1676
magnesium oxide	MgO	2852	3600
water	H_2O	0	100
ethanol	C_2H_5OH	–114	78.3
ammonia	NH_3	–78	–33.3
nitrogen	N_2	–210	–196
carbon tetrachloride	CCl_4	–23	77

1. Create a bar graph for the melting point data shown above.

2. What type of compounds are NaI, $CaCl_2$, LiBr, and MgO?

3. What type of compounds are C_2H_5OH, NH_3, N_2, and CCl_4?

_____

4. How do the melting and boiling points of ionic compounds compare to those of covalent compounds? Note two things that you notice about the temperatures.

_____

_____

_____

_____

5. Why do you think there is such a huge difference in the melting points of ionic and covalent compounds?

_____

_____

_____

6. What is the relationship between the melting point and the strength of the bonds that hold the atoms together?

_____

7. Which compound, magnesium oxide or sodium iodide, requires more energy to overcome the electrostatic forces holding the ions together in the lattice structure? Explain your choice.

_____

_____

8. Based on their melting points, what can you infer about the state of ionic compounds at room temperature?

_____

9. Analyze the data given. In what state are covalent compounds at room temperature?

_____

10. Methane, CH_4, has a melting point of –182 °C and a boiling point of –164 °C. Predict whether methane is a covalent or an ionic compound.

_____

Covalent Bonding

Use with textbook pages 148–149.

1. **Base Word, Suffixes, and Word Parts**

   To understand an unfamiliar word, try breaking it down into smaller parts. Then, determine what each part means. If the word is made up of a prefix, a base, and a suffix, break the word down to identify these three components. Refer to the words *diatomic molecule* on page 148 in the textbook.

   a) In the word *diatomic*, what is the prefix? _____

   b) What do you think this prefix means? _____

   c) In the word *diatomic*, what is the base word? _____

   d) What do you think the suffix is? _____

   e) What does this suffix mean? _____

   f) Put together your answers to parts a) to e) to explain what *diatomic molecule* means.

   _____

2. **Visualizing**

   Visualizing means forming an image in your mind based on the text that you are reading. The following table shows the steps for visualizing the concepts while reading the paragraph about diatomic molecules and covalent bonds on page 148 in the textbook. Complete the table.

Steps	How I Form a Picture in My Mind
1. Start with a part of the text that is familiar.	
2. Look for specifics in the text to make your picture more accurate.	
3. Once you have created a picture in your mind, sketch it.	

3. **Check for Understanding**

   Create a mnemonic to help you remember the seven elements that exist as diatomic molecules. An example of a mnemonic is: "**H**ere **i**n **B**ritish **C**olumbia, **N**ear **O**ur **F**riends."

   _____

2.4 Assessment

Match each term on the left with the best description on the right. Each descriptor may be used only once.

Term	Description
1. ____ molecule	A. bond that forms when atoms share electrons
2. ____ ionic bond	B. a compound that consists of a metallic ion and a non-metallic ion
3. ____ covalent bond	C. a particle that has two or more atoms held together by covalent bonds
4. ____ ionic compound	D. bond that forms between a positively charged ion and a negatively charged ion
5. ____ covalent compound	E. a compound that consists of two or more elements that are covalently bonded together

Circle the letter of the best answer for questions 6 to 16.

6. Which of the following represents a diatomic molecule?

    A. H^+

    B. F_2

    C. KI

    D. H_2O

7. Which of the following correctly shows an example of an ionic compound and a covalent compound?

	Ionic Compound	Covalent Compound
A.	H_2	CO_2
B.	$SrCl_2$	CH_4
C.	$C_6H_{12}O_6$	NaOH
D.	$KMnO_4$	RbCl

8. Which of following will have ionic bonds holding the compound together?

    A. ozone, O_3

    B. ethanol, C_2H_6O

    C. sucrose, $C_{12}H_{22}O_{11}$

    D. beryllium sulfide, BeS

9. Which of the following correctly describes what happens when a magnesium atom and an oxygen atom form a compound?

    A. A magnesium atom transfers its valence electrons to an oxygen atom.

    B. An oxygen atom transfers its valence electrons to a magnesium atom.

    C. A magnesium atom shares its valence electrons with an oxygen atom.

    D. A magnesium atom and an oxygen atom both switch valence electrons with each other.

10. Which of the following compounds has a lattice structure?

   A. CO

   B. CCl_4

   C. ZnS

   D. H_2O

11. Calcium fluoride is a crystalline solid at room temperature. What accounts for this compound being hard and brittle?

   A. the low melting point of the compound

   B. the sharing of the electrons between calcium and fluorine

   C. the repulsive force between the calcium and fluoride ions

   D. the strength of the ionic bond that holds the calcium and fluoride ions together

12. Which of the following correctly compares the melting points of ionic compounds to covalent compounds?

	Ionic Compound	Covalent Compound
A.	Has low melting point	Has low melting point
B.	Has high melting point	Has high melting point
C.	Has low melting point	Has high melting point
D.	Has high melting point	Has low melting point

13. Which of the following explains why potassium bromide (KBr) has a high melting point of 734 °C?

   A. It requires high temperatures to form the lattices.

   B. It requires a lot of energy to break the ionic bonds.

   C. It requires high temperatures to maintain the strong electrostatic forces.

   D. It requires a lot of energy to produce forces of repulsion to break the crystals.

14. Which of the following will allow an electric current to flow through it?

   A. a beaker of distilled water, H_2O

   B. a beaker of solid lithium chloride, LiCl

   C. a beaker of methanol solution, CH_3OH

   D. a beaker of lithium chloride solution, LiCl

15. Which of the following describes ways that atoms can become stable?

I	an iodine atom loses one electron
II	a calcium atom loses two electrons
III	two bromine atoms share electrons

    A. I and II only

    B. I and III only

    C. II and III only

    D. I, II, and III

16. Which of the following is a property of both ionic and covalent compounds?

    A. low boiling points

    B. full valence shells

    C. sharing of electrons

    D. transferring of electrons

17. Complete the mind map for ionic and covalent compounds.

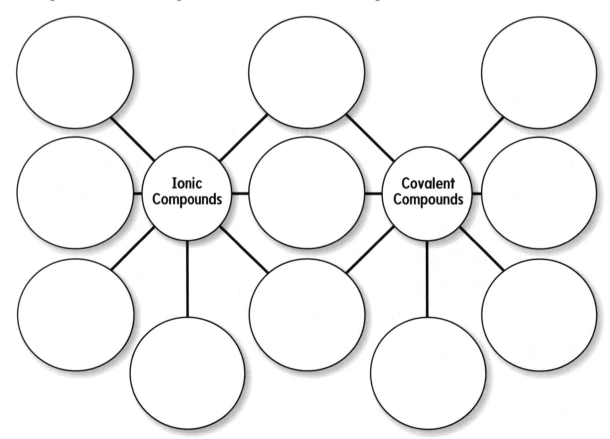

How do we name and write formulas for compounds?

Use with textbook pages 154–173.

Naming Binary Ionic Compounds

A **binary ionic compound** consists of two elements (a metal ion and a non-metal ion) held together by strong **ionic bonds**. To name a binary ionic compound, write the element name of the positive metal ion first. Then, write the name of the negative non-metal ion with a suffix *-ide*. Refer to Table 2.5 on page 157 of the textbook to see a list of some common non-metal ions.

Writing Chemical Formulas for Ionic Compounds

The **chemical formula** of an ionic compound uses subscripts to show the number of metal ions and non-metal ions there are in the compound. The subscript appears to the right of the element chemical symbol. Refer to Figure 2.38 on page 158 of the textbook to see what a typical chemical formula looks like with subscripts. When there is no subscript, that is assumed to be 1. To write a chemical formula, you must balance the charges of the metal ion and the non-metal ion. The *ion charges* of each element can be found on the periodic table. Refer to the Sample Problem on page 160 of the textbook to review the steps used to write the chemical formula for ionic compounds.

Multivalent Metals

Multivalent metals are metals with more than one possible ion charge. Their different ion charges are indicated by *Roman numerals* after the name. Table 2.6 on page 162 of the textbook shows Roman numerals for 1 to 7. When writing the name of an ionic compound with a multivalent metal, a Roman numeral must be used to indicate the particular ion charge in that compound. Refer to the Sample Problem on page 163 of the textbook to review the steps used to name ionic compounds involving a multivalent metal.

Polyatomic Ions

A **polyatomic ion** is an ion that consists of two or more atoms held together by covalent bonds. When writing the name of an ionic compound with a polyatomic ion in it, the name of the positive ion is written first followed by the name of the negative ion. Table 2.7 on page 164 of the textbook lists the names of some common polyatomic ions. Refer to the Sample Problem on page 165 of the textbook to review the steps on how to write the chemical formulas of a compound with a polyatomic ion.

Covalent Compounds

A **binary covalent compound** has only two elements held together by covalent bonds. To write the chemical formula for these compounds, write the element symbol in the order in which it appears in the name. When writing the name of a covalent compound, prefixes are used. Refer to page 169 of the textbook to see the prefixes in Table 2.8, and the steps for writing the name and formula of covalent compounds.

Writing Chemical Names and Formulas of Ionic Compounds

Use with textbook pages 154–161.

You can use the periodic table on page 106 to help you answer these questions.

1. Define the following terms:

a) ion

_____

b) ionic bond

_____

_____

c) binary ionic compound

_____

_____

2. Write the formulas for the ionic compounds formed from the following positive and negative ions. Then name the binary ionic compounds.

	Ions	Chemical Formula	Compound Name
a)	Li^+ F^-		
b)	Be^{2+} Br^-		
c)	Na^+ O^{2-}		
d)	Sc^{3+} I^-		
e)	Mg^{2+} S^{2-}		
f)	K^+ P^{3-}		
g)	Ca^{2+} N^{3-}		
h)	Al^{3+} Br^-		
i)	Ba^{2+} Se^{2-}		
j)	Zn^{2+} O^{2-}		

3. Write the names of the following ionic compounds.

a) RbI _____

b) Cs_2O _____

c) SrS _____

d) $BaCl_2$ _____

e) InP _____

f) Li_3N _____

g) $MgBr_2$ _____

h) CaO _____

i) KCl _____

j) $ZrSe_2$ _____

4. Write the chemical formulas for the following ionic compounds.

a) cesium fluoride _____

b) beryllium phosphide _____

c) aluminum oxide _____

d) strontium bromide _____

e) gallium nitride _____

f) zinc sulfide _____

g) rubidium iodide _____

h) silver chloride _____

i) cadmium oxide _____

Ionic Compounds with Multivalent Metals

Use with textbook pages 162–163.

You can use the periodic table on page 106 and Roman numerals listed on page 162 to help you answer these questions.

1. Write the formulas and names of the ionic compounds with the following combination of ions. The table has been partially completed to help guide you.

	Positive Ion	Negative Ion	Chemical Formula	Compound Name
a)	Ti^{3+}	Cl^-		
b)				iron(II) oxide
c)			$PdBr_2$	
d)	Sn^{4+}	F^-		
e)				gold(I) chloride
f)	Pt^{4+}	O^{2-}		
g)			CoF_2	
h)				nickel(II) iodide
i)	Nb^{3+}	N^{3-}		
j)			MnO_2	

2. Write the chemical formulas for the following ionic compounds.

   a) cobalt(III) fluoride _____

   b) osmium(IV) chloride _____

   c) chromium(III) oxide _____

   d) mercury(II) selenide _____

   e) copper(II) chloride _____

   f) lead(II) sulfide _____

   g) titanium(III) nitride _____

   h) bismuth(III) sulfide _____

   i) ruthenium(IV) oxide _____

   j) nickel(II) fluoride _____

3. Write the names of the following ionic compounds.

   a) $NbCl_5$ _____

   b) SnF_4 _____

   c) Mn_2O_3 _____

   d) $RhCl_3$ _____

   e) NiF_3 _____

   f) HgS _____

   g) TlI _____

   h) IrO_2 _____

   i) $FeCl_2$ _____

   j) V_2O_5 _____

Ionic Compounds with Polyatomic Ions

Use with textbook pages 164–165.

You can use the periodic table on page 106 and the list of polyatomic ions on page 164 to help you answer these questions.

1. Complete the following table by providing the correct chemical formula for each compound formed from the ions indicated.

Formulas for Some Ionic Compounds				
	fluoride	hydroxide	carbonate	phosphate
a) sodium				
b) aluminum				
c) copper(II)				
d) manganese(IV)				
e) ammonium				

2. Write the chemical formulas for the following ionic compounds.

   a) barium chlorite _____

   b) nickel(II) nitrate _____

   c) potassium chromate _____

   d) lead(IV) phosphate _____

   e) cadmium peroxide _____

   f) copper(I) carbonate _____

   g) chromium(III) sulfite _____

   h) calcium phosphite _____

   i) iron(III) acetate _____

   j) strontium permanganate _____

3. Write the names of the following ionic compounds.

   a) $V(ClO_3)_4$ _____

   b) $Al_2(CO_3)_3$ _____

   c) $Co(NO_2)_2$ _____

   d) $(NH_4)_2SO_4$ _____

   e) $Ti(CrO_4)_2$ _____

   f) Li_3PO_4 _____

   g) $Cr(MnO_4)_3$ _____

   h) $Ag_2Cr_2O_7$ _____

   i) $Mg(HCO_3)_2$ _____

   j) $Sn(OH)_4$ _____

Covalent Compounds

Use with textbook pages 168–172.

1. Write the chemical formula for each of the following binary covalent compounds.

   a) sulfur dioxide _____

   b) carbon tetrafluoride _____

   c) selenium trioxide _____

   d) nitrogen trichloride _____

   e) carbon dioxide _____

   f) boron trifluoride _____

   g) tetrasulfur tetranitride _____

   h) diphosphorus pentoxide _____

   i) carbon disulfide _____

   j) nitrogen monoxide _____

   k) diarsenic trioxide _____

   l) sulfur hexafluoride _____

2. Write the name for each of the following binary covalent compounds.

   a) Cl_2O_7 _____

   b) N_2O_4 _____

   c) SO_3 _____

   d) PCl_5 _____

   e) NF_3 _____

   f) CS_2 _____

   g) SiF_4 _____

   h) N_2O_3 _____

   i) BI_3 _____

   j) ClF_3 _____

   k) SCl_2 _____

   l) CO _____

Ionic Compounds in Fireworks

Use with textbook pages 154–165.

Use the following reading passage to answer questions 1 to 4.

The Celebration of Lights is the world's longest-running fireworks competition. Every summer, hundreds of thousands of spectators gather around English Bay and Kitsilano for Vancouver's iconic annual festival. It is a favourite tradition for many Vancouverites. People are entertained for three nights by spectacular displays of world-class pyrotechnics, perfectly choreographed to music. Three countries compete each year to wow the audience.

The firework aerial shells are launched from a barge floating in English Bay. An aerial shell is a small tube that contains the explosive chemicals that make up the fireworks. Each aerial shell has small explosive stars arranged in specific patterns in gunpowder. The gunpowder is made up of mostly potassium nitrate. The stars have explosives that give the fireworks their spectacular colours when they explode in the sky. The fireworks have specific shapes based on the patterns in which the stars are packaged in the aerial shells. Bright red chrysanthemum spinners light up the night sky as a result of the ignition of strontium carbonate. Bursts of blue peonies are due to copper(I) chloride. Green sprays are the result of the explosion of barium chloride.

1. Asking Questions

While reading the two paragraphs above, stop to ask who, what, when, where, why, and how questions. Write these six questions down. See if your questions are answered in the text. If they are not, reread the paragraphs to see if you misunderstood a concept. This will allow you to make connections beyond the text.

a) Who _____

_____

b) What _____

_____

c) Where _____

_____

d) When _____

_____

e) Why _____

_____

2. Monitoring Comprehension

a) List four ionic compounds used in fireworks and give their chemical formulas.

_____

_____

_____

b) What are some chemical properties that all four of these ionic compounds have in common?

_____

_____

c) Name three forms of energy that are involved during a firework display.

_____

_____

_____

3. Identifying Cause and Effect

a) Read the second paragraph and explain why the arrangements of the stars inside the aerial shells are important for the outcome of the visual display of the fireworks show.

_____

_____

_____

b) A burst of bright red chrysanthemum illuminates the sky. What chemical is responsible for the colour of this fireworks explosion?

_____

4. Research some of the challenges present when attempting to synchronize music to a fireworks display.

2.5 Assessment

Match each term on the left with the best description on the right. Each descriptor may be used only once.

Term	Description
1. ____ ion bond	**A.** a bond that forms when atoms share electrons
2. ____ covalent bond	**B.** a metal that can have more than one ion charge
3. ____ polyatomic ion	**C.** a bond that holds a positively charged ion together with a negatively charged ion
4. ____ multivalent metal	**D.** an ion that consists of more than two different elements covalently bonded together
5. ____ binary ionic compound	**E.** a compound that consists of a positively charged ion and a negatively charged ion held together by ionic bonds
6. ____ binary covalent compound	**F.** a compound that consists of non-metals that result in the sharing of electrons and are held together by covalent bonds

Circle the letter of the best answer for questions 7 to 20.

7. When selenium combines with a metal, it forms an ionic compound. This compound's name ends in

A. selenite.

B. selenate.

C. selenide.

D. selenium.

8. Which of the following correctly describes the components of the compound ScF_3?

I	Scandium is the positive metal ion.
II	Fluoride is the negative non-metal ion.
III	The ratio of the ions in this compound is 1 Sc^{3+} ion : 3 F^- ions.

A. I and II only

B. I and III only

C. II and III only

D. I, II, and III

9. In the chemical formula Ga_2O_3, the subscripts indicate that

A. there are two gallium ions and three oxygen ions in the compound.

B. there are three gallium ions and two oxygen ions in the compound.

C. gallium has an ion charge of 2^- and oxygen has an ion charge of 3^+.

D. gallium has an ion charge of 2^+ and oxygen has an ion charge of 3^-.

10. What are the subscripts when an alkaline-earth metal forms an ionic compound with a halogen?

   A. 1 and 1   **C.** 1 and 3

   B. 1 and 2   **D.** 2 and 3

11. Determine the ratio of the metal ion to the non-metal ion for calcium oxide, which is used to remove sulfur dioxide from power plant exhaust.

   A. $1:1$ **C.** $1:3$

   B. $1:2$ **D.** $2:3$

12. What does the Roman numeral in tin(II) nitride indicate?

   A. Tin has an ion charge of 2^+.

   B. Tin has an ion charge of 2^-.

   C. There are two tin molecules.

   D. There are two tin atoms in the compound.

13. What is the chemical formula for strontium chloride, a chemical used in fireworks?

   A. $SrCl$ **C.** $SrCl_2$

   B. Sr_2Cl **D.** Sr_2Cl_2

14. Name the compound Mg_3N_2 that is used to make special glass.

   A. magnesium nitride   **C.** magnesium(III) nitride

   B. magnesium nitrogen   **D.** trimagnesium dinitride

15. Determine the chemical formula for barium hydroxide, a substance used in soap.

   A. $BaOH$ **C.** Ba_2OH

   B. $BaOH_2$ **D.** $Ba(OH)_2$

16. Name the compound, $KMnO_4$, that is used to clean wounds.

   A. potassium permanganate   **C.** potassium manganese oxide

   B. potassium(I) permanganate   **D.** potassium manganese tetraoxide

17. Give the chemical formula for silver(I) acetate, a substance used in anti-smoking drugs.

   A. $AgCH_3COO$ **C.** $(Ag)CH_3COO$

   B. $AgCH_3COO^-$ **D.** $Ag(CH_3COO)_2$

18. What is the name for the compound $Pb(CO_3)_2$?

    A. lead carbonate   **C.** lead(II) carbonate

    B. lead dicarbonate   **D.** lead(IV) carbonate

19. What is the chemical formula for the drying agent diphosphorus pentoxide?

    A. PO   **C.** P_2O_5

    B. P_2O_4 **D.** P_5O_2

20. Name the compound NF_3.

    A. nitrogen fluoride   **C.** mononitrogen trifluoride

    B. nitrogen trifluoride   **D.** trinitrogen monofluoride

21. Compare and contrast how to write the chemical name for a covalent compound and an ionic compound. Complete the graphic organizer shown below.

COMPARE AND CONTRAST

Main Topic
Writing Chemical Names

Subtopic
Covalent Compound

Subtopic
Ionic Compound

ALIKE

Use element names in compound name

DIFFERENT

How does the periodic table fit into a smartphone?

What's the Issue?

Over 20 years ago, only a small fraction of the population owned a cell phone. Given the fact that over one billion smartphones were sold worldwide in 2016, it is evident that there is a global demand for these portable communcation devices. People use their smartphones to talk to their friends, send text messages, take photos, listen to the latest hits, and surf the internet while out and about. Dozens of elements on the periodic table make this possible.

Alkali metals, alkaline-earth metals, halogens, lanthanides, transition metals, and metals from Groups 13 to 16 all contribute to the look and feel of a smartphone. Most people like touchscreen technology because it is easy to use. Indium (III) oxide and tin(II) oxide make up a film that allows electricity to flow so that the screen can operate as a touch screen. The glass screen, made of silicon, oxygen, and aluminum, is strengthened with the addition of potassium ions so that it is more durable. The properties of rare-earth metals are key to the innovative features of the smartphones. They are the essential ingredients to making these devices light, vivid, and loud. The matrix of vibrant colourful icons on the touchscreen is due to a variety of rare-earth metals (yttrium, lanthanum, praseodymium, europium, gadolinium, terbium, and dysprosium). Some of these rare-earth metals also prevent UV light from penetrating the phone. Neodynium, terbium, and dysprosium are used in magnets of the vibration unit to make smartphones vibrate when a call comes in. Praseodymium, neodymium, gadolinium, terbium, and dysprosium are all used in the speakers and the microphone. Most of the rare-earth metals used to make smartphones are mined in China.

Silicon, antimony, gallium, oxygen, and arsenic are used to make a powerful chip that controls the operation of the entire smartphone. Gold, silver, and tantalum are used in the electrical components. Copper wiring connects all of these components. Smartphones are powered by a lithium ion battery that uses lithium cobalt oxide on the positive terminal and carbon on the negative terminal. The batteries are encased in aluminum, while the smartphone casing is made of magnesium and plastic compounds.

It is hard to imagine life without smartphones. While people enjoy the convenience that these devices provide, most of us don't think about the amount of time that went into the research, design, and construction of these devices. Smartphones have impacted our lives dramatically and are constantly evolving as technology advances.

Dig Deeper

Collaborate with your classmates to explore one or more of these questions—or generate your own questions to explore.

1. How do tech companies decide what features to include in a smartphone to enhance the experience for its users? Research the process of designing and constructing a smartphone.

2. What are some physical and chemical properties that tech companies should consider when choosing the best material to build smartphones? Why is this important?

3. Research the physical and chemical properties of lithium. Find out why the majority of smartphones use lithium ion batteries. Does it provide the best performance and longest battery life? How do lithium's physical and chemical properties relate to the ways industries use it?

4. What are some environmental issues associated with the mining and processing of rare-earth metals?

5. List some environmental efforts enforced by governments to help reduce the ecological damage caused by the mining of rare-earth metals. Research some cleaner, greener rare-earth mining practices.

6. What are some concerns related to the disposal of smartphones once people are done with them? What recycling programs are in place in your community? How are tech companies promoting social responsibility in this matter?

7. What factors should be considered when deciding whether to purchase a new smartphone?

8. Imagine you were hired by a major tech company to design a new smartphone. Research some features and innovations that you would like to see in this new device.

How is electrical energy part of your world?

Use with textbook pages 188-199.

Different Forms of Energy

We rely on **electrical energy** to run numerous devices and equipment. This electrical energy is transformed from other types of energy.

- Mechanical energy is the sum of kinetic energy and potential energy. Any moving object has kinetic energy. Potential energy is stored energy of a system because of its position or condition. For example, the water at the top of a waterfall, just before it falls, has potential energy because of its position, and kinetic energy because it is moving.

- Chemical energy is stored in chemical bonds and released in chemical reactions. Chemical energy is stored in batteries, as well as fossil fuels. Chemical energy stored in animals and plants is called biomass.

- Solar energy is carried by electromagnetic radiation from the Sun. Fossil fuels and biomass are the result of plants and plant-like organisms capturing solar energy.

- Nuclear energy is generated by the formation of new atoms. In nuclear fusion, new atoms are made as smaller atoms collide and fuse. In nuclear fission, new atoms are made by splitting larger atoms. Fusion reactions occur in stars, including the Sun. Fission reactions occur in nuclear reactors.

- Thermal energy is due to the rapid motion of particles. We detect it as heat. Earth's interior is a source of thermal energy called geothermal energy.

Main Methods of Generating Electrical Energy

Most of the electrical energy used in Canada is generated from river flow, fossil fuels, and nuclear reactions.

- River flow has kinetic energy, the energy of motion. The kinetic energy of the moving water turns the turbine of a **generator system** to generate electrical energy. The figure below shows how a generator system works.

Turbine: Steam, water, or wind cause the turbine to spin.

Shaft: The shaft connects the turbine to the generator. As the turbine spins, it makes the shaft spin.

Generator: The kinetic energy of the spinning shaft is transformed into electrical energy inside the generator. This happens when energy from the shaft turns a wire loop or coil. A magnet surrounds the rotating wire, as shown in the inset. As the wire turns, electrons flow in the wire. This flow of electrons powers electrical devices.

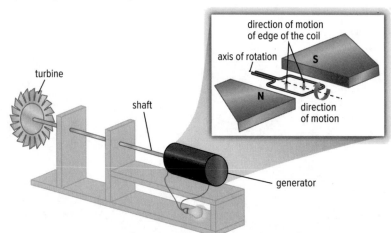

- Energy from burning fossil fuels and nuclear fission reactions is also used to generate electrical energy using generator systems.

The figure below shows how river flow, fossil fuels, and nuclear reactions can be used to generate electrical energy. What role does thermal energy play in generating electrical energy from fossil fuels and nuclear reactions?

Hydroelectric Energy from River Flow

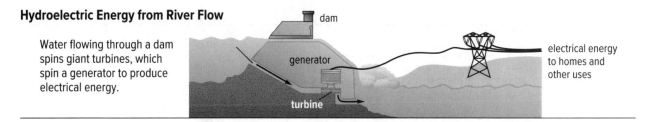

Water flowing through a dam spins giant turbines, which spin a generator to produce electrical energy.

Electrical Energy from Fossil Fuels

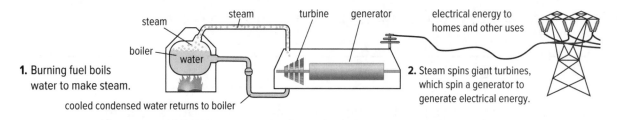

1. Burning fuel boils water to make steam.

2. Steam spins giant turbines, which spin a generator to generate electrical energy.

Electrical Energy from Nuclear Reactions

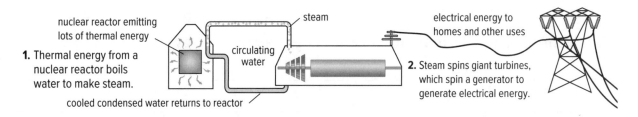

1. Thermal energy from a nuclear reactor boils water to make steam.

2. Steam spins giant turbines, which spin a generator to generate electrical energy.

Other Methods of Generating Electrical Energy

- Photovoltaic cells are made of special materials that transform solar energy into electrical energy.

- Wind has kinetic energy. This energy is transformed into electrical energy as moving air turns the turbine of a generator system.

- Thermal energy from molten rock under Earth's crust generates steam that can be used to turn turbines to generate electrical energy.

- The rise and fall of waves can compress an air column, which can turn a turbine to generate electrical energy. Moving water associated with tides can also spin turbines.

Different Types of Energy

Use with textbook pages 192–193.

Determine if each statement below is true or false. If a statement is false, write the correct statement in the space provided.

1. Mechanical energy is the sum of kinetic energy and chemical energy.

_____

_____

2. Fusion reactions are carried out in reactors on Earth.

_____

_____

3. Chemical energy is released when a chemical reaction occurs.

_____

_____

4. One type of energy cannot be transformed into another type of energy.

_____

_____

5. Chemical energy from Earth's interior is geothermal energy.

_____

_____

6. Solar energy is carried by electromagnetic radiation given off by the Sun.

_____

_____

7. Positional energy is stored energy that a system has due to its position or condition.

_____

_____

Energy In Your Life

Use with textbook pages 192–193.

Use the following reading passage to answer questions 1 and 2.

You are visiting Harrison Hot Springs in southern B.C. in late winter. Canada geese are waddling around and driftwood litters the beach that skirts Harrison Lake. It's a chilly day despite the afternoon sunlight. As you walk along the path, you notice the strong wind whipping up waves off shore. If only it were warmer, it would be perfect for wind surfing. You turn on your cellphone for some music, thankful you remembered to recharge the battery this morning. You walk toward the marina, stopping to grab a hot chocolate along the way. You pop into the art gallery and look at the work of a local photographer that is on display. A photo showing a beach near Tofino at low tide catches your eye.

As you continue your walk, you notice water cascading down the cliff beside the road in small waterfalls. The Sun has now slipped behind the mountain on the western shore of the lake and the moon has risen. It's time to head back and warm up in the hot springs pool. It will be just the thing after your chilly winter walk.

1. Mark the Text

You encountered many different examples of things that carry or store energy on your walk. Highlight 10 examples in the reading passage.

2. Identifying Concepts

Use your examples from question 1 to complete the table. The first row has been done for you. Note that some examples may involve more than one type of energy. For instance, a tree transforms solar energy into chemical energy through photosynthesis.

	Example	Type of Energy	Explanation of Energy Type
a)	Canada geese	Chemical energy	The geese are animals. Animals are a form of biomass. Biomass stores chemical energy.
b)			
c)			
d)			
e)			
f)			
g)			
h)			
i)			
j)			

Generating Electrical Energy

Use with textbook page 195.

1. Write a caption that explains how electrical energy is being generated in each diagram below.

a)

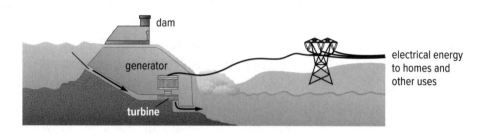

_____

_____

_____

b)

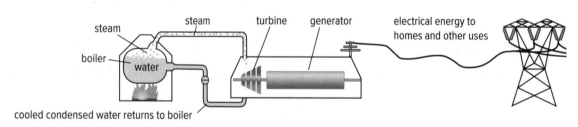

_____

_____

_____

c)

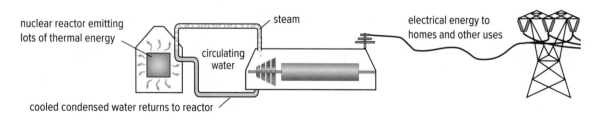

_____

_____

_____

Technology Fair

Use with textbook page 196.

1. Use the terms in the box below to complete the reading passage that follows. There is one extra term.

photovoltaic effect	controller
potential energy	anemometer
generator system	solar energy
kinetic energy	electromagnetic radiation

You are visiting a technology fair at the University of Northern British Columbia. The first exhibit you stop at is a display of photovoltaic cells. These cells transform _____ into electrical energy. The exhibitor explains that the cells are made of special materials that produce electrical energy when they are exposed to light. This phenomenon is called the _____. You are surprised to learn that photovoltaic cells only transform the energy of visible light to electrical energy. After all, the Sun emits many different types of _____. However, the exhibitor explains that scientists are currently working to create cells that transform other types into electrical energy. The second exhibit has an enormous wind turbine. The exhibitor explains how the _____ of wind is transformed into electrical energy as the moving air turns the turbine that is part of a(n) _____. For safety, a(n) _____ shuts the turbine down when the wind speed reaches 90 km/h. Intrigued, you ask the exhibitor how the turbine knows when to shut down. The exhibitor replies that a(n) _____ is used to measure wind speed.

3.1 Assessment

Match each description on the left with the type of energy it best matches on the right. Each type of energy may be used only once.

Description	Type of Energy
1. ____ geysers, hot springs, and volcanoes	A. solar energy
2. ____ water at the top of a waterfall	B. potential energy
3. ____ wind, river flow, and waves	C. nuclear energy
4. ____ sunlight	D. kinetic energy
5. ____ trees, batteries, and natural gas	E. thermal energy
6. ____ fission and fusion	F. chemical energy

Circle the letter of the best answer for questions 7 to 22.

7. Which parts of the human body rely on electrical signals to work?

I	heart
II	muscles
III	eyes

A. I and II only

B. I and III only

C. II and III only

D. I, II, and III

8. How does a capacitive touch-sensitive screen work on a tablet?

A. The pressure from a touch command completes an electrical pathway.

B. When the user's finger touches the screen, a tiny electrical charge passes through it to complete an electrical pathway.

C. The pressure from a touch command generates a magnetic field.

D. When the user's finger touches the screen, a flexible plastic expands and contracts.

9. What causes a maglev train to levitate?

A. electrical coils create magnetic fields that repel large magnets under the train

B. nuclear propulsion

C. upward jets of compressed air

D. antigravitational acceleration

10. Scientists have developed a plastic that expands and contracts slightly in response to electrical energy. What has this enabled scientists to build?

   A. maglev trains

   B. capacitive touch-sensitive screens

   C. photovoltaic cells

   D. robots with human-like hand and facial movements

11. You stir some cream into a cup of warm coffee with a spoon. What types of energy are evident in this example?

   A. kinetic and thermal energy

   B. potential and kinetic energy

   C. kinetic, thermal, and chemical energy

   D. kinetic, thermal, and mechanical energy

12. What type of reactions occur in the Sun?

   A. solar reactions

   B. fusion reactions

   C. fission reactions

   D. thermal reactions

13. Thermal energy is generated through the rapid motion of the particles that make up an object. Based on this description, what other type of energy could thermal energy be classified as?

   A. potential energy

   B. kinetic energy

   C. mechanical energy

   D. chemical energy

14. Which of the following types of energy is released by forming new atoms?

   A. nuclear energy

   B. chemical energy

   C. atomic energy

   D. formation energy

15. A calculator uses a photovoltaic cell and a backup battery. Which of the following types of energy does the calculator use?

I	solar energy
II	chemical energy
III	kinetic energy

A. I and II only

C. II and III only

B. I and III only

D. I, II, and III

16. B.C. student Ann Makosinski designed a cup that can charge a cellphone when it is filled with a hot beverage. What type of energy does this invention most likely transform into electrical energy?

A. potential energy

C. mechanical energy

B. thermal energy

D. chemical energy

17. Which of the following are components of a generator system?

I	turbine
II	shaft
III	generator

A. I and II only

C. II and III only

B. I and III only

D. I, II, and III

18. Which type of energy is transformed into electrical energy by a generator system?

A. potential energy

C. rotational energy

B. kinetic energy

D. mechanical energy

19. Which of the following statements is true about energy?

A. It can be created.

C. It can be transformed.

B. It can be destroyed.

D. All of the above.

20. Which of the following are used to generate electrical energy in British Columbia?

I	nuclear reactions
II	fossil fuels
III	river flow

A. I and II only

C. II and III only

B. I and III only

D. I, II, and III

21. What role does thermal energy play in the generation of electrical energy from nuclear reactions?

   A. Thermal energy from the reactions is used to boil water into steam, which turns a turbine of a generator system.

   B. Thermal energy causes the nuclear reactions to take place.

   C. Thermal energy is used to turn the turbine of the generator system.

   D. It plays no role.

22. Which of the following is true of photovoltaic cells?

   A. They are made of thin layers of quartz crystals.

   B. They generate electrical energy when visible light strikes their surface.

   C. They generate electrical energy when any type of electromagnetic radiation strikes their surface.

   D. They can only be used to run small devices, like calculators.

23. Complete the following flowchart to explain how electrical energy is generated by photovoltaic cells.

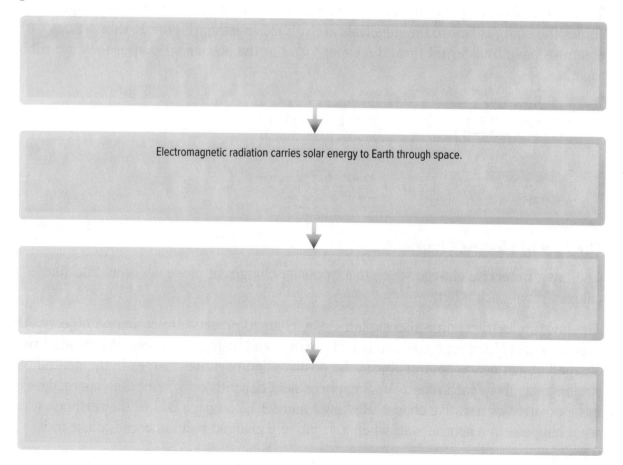

Electromagnetic radiation carries solar energy to Earth through space.

How do electrical charges behave?

Use with textbook pages 202–209.

The Nature of Electrical Charges

Positive charges are the charges of protons. Protons are part of the nucleus of atoms and are held firmly in place. They cannot be rubbed off when materials are rubbed together. **Negative charges** are the charges of electrons. Electrons can be rubbed off, because they surround the nucleus and some are not tightly bound to it. When electrons are rubbed off a material, it becomes positively charged. The material that gains electrons becomes negatively charged. Charging a material by rubbing is called charging by friction.

Electrically Neutral and Electrically Charged Materials

- Before two materials are rubbed together, they have equal numbers of positively charged protons and negatively charged electrons. The equal numbers of positive and negative charges cancel each other out, so the materials are electrically neutral.

- When two materials are rubbed together, electrons can be transferred. If electrons are rubbed off one material, the protons stay behind and the material becomes electrically charged. So does the material that gains the electrons. A material that is electrically charged has an unequal number of positive and negative charges.

This figure shows a paper towel on top and an acetate strip on the bottom. Figure A shows the charges before the materials are rubbed together. Figure B shows that electrons have transferred from the paper towel to the acetate strip after they are rubbed together.

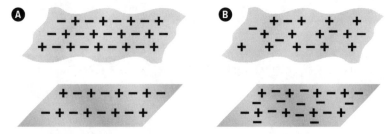

The Law of Electric Charge

The **law of electric charge** states that opposite charges attract each other and like charges repel each other.

The law of electric charge also explains why charged objects attract neutral objects. All neutral objects have an equal number of positive and negative charges. When you bring a charged object near a neutral object, the positive and negative charges in the neutral object stretch apart from each other. What happens next depends on whether the charged object has a positive or negative charge. Review Figure 3.12 on page 207 of the textbook to see what happens to a neutral wall when a negatively charged balloon comes close to it.

Charging by Friction

Use with textbook pages 204–207.

1. **a)** Plus and minus signs are often used to represent positive and negative charges. Add plus and minus signs to the cloud to show what happens to positive and negative charges in a storm cloud when it becomes charged by friction.

b) Write a caption to explain how charging by friction has occurred in the above diagram.

_____

_____

_____

_____

_____

_____

2. Write a caption to explain the role that charging by friction has played in the cartoon.

_____

_____

_____

_____

_____

An Application of Electrical Charges

Use with textbook pages 204–207.

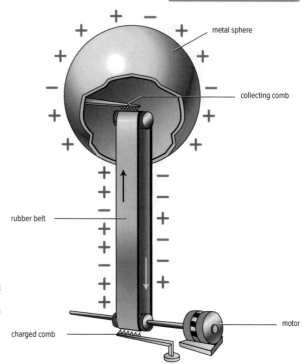

metal sphere

collecting comb

rubber belt

charged comb

motor

Use the text below to answer questions 1 and 2.

A Van de Graaff generator is a device that can build up and transfer a large amount of charge. Physicist Robert Van de Graaff invented it in 1929. Inside an insulated column, a rubber belt moves over two rollers. A motor drives the lower roller, and, as the belt moves over it, charging by friction occurs. The charges are carried upward as the belt rotates. A metal collecting comb is found near the top roller. The comb is attached to the inside of a metal sphere sitting on the column. The charged belt induces a redistribution of charges in the comb, and charges accumulate on the metal sphere.

Van de Graaff generators have various applications. For example, they have been used to break apart atoms since the 1930s. A Van de Graaff generator can accelerate particles to very high speeds. Beams of high-speed particles can be focussed so they crash into each other, breaking the atoms into fragments and sometimes forming new subatomic particles. Van de Graaff generators have also been used to test electronic circuitry in space technology.

1. **Identifying the Main Idea and Details**

   The main ideas of a text are supported and explained by details, such as facts or examples. It is important to be able to differentiate between the main idea and its supporting details. Phrases such as *for example* and *for instance* are clues that a detail will follow. If you cannot decide whether a sentence is the main idea or a detail, ask yourself, "Is this information the most important thing I need to know, or does this information help me understand the most important thing?"

   a) Write the main idea of the first paragraph in the text about the Van de Graaff generator.

   _____

   _____

   _____

b) Write two supporting details.

_____

_____

_____

_____

c) Write the main idea of the second paragraph.

_____

_____

d) Write two supporting details.

_____

_____

_____

_____

2. Interpreting Diagrams

A diagram is a simplified drawing that shows a concept or a process. Diagrams can help readers understand complex ideas or explanations. Symbols are a common feature of diagrams. In this Unit, a plus sign (+) is used to indicate a positive electric charge. A minus sign (–) is used to indicate a negative electric charge.

Examine the diagram of the Van de Graaff generator. If the metal sphere becomes positively charged, why does this diagram show some minus signs on the sphere?

_____

_____

_____

_____

The Law of Electric Charge

Use with textbook pages 206–207.

1. a) Balloon A has been given a positive charge. Add plus and minus signs to the balloon to indicate this.

b) Balloon B is electrically neutral. Add plus and minus signs to the balloon to indicate this.

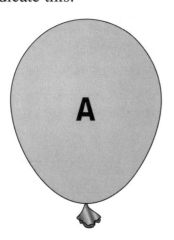

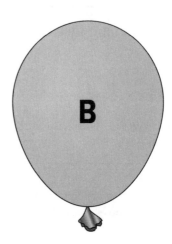

c) Balloons A and B are attracted to each other. Add plus and minus signs to the diagram to show the location of the charges.

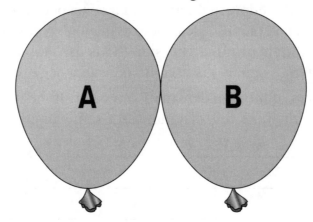

d) Write a caption explaining why the balloons behave as they do.

_____

_____

_____

_____

Using Terminology

Use with textbook pages 204–207.

Match each description below with Image A (before hair is rubbed with a balloon) or
Image B (after hair is rubbed with a balloon). Write each description on the lines provided.

electrically neutral	no charge transfer
charge transfer	electrically charged
attraction	no attraction

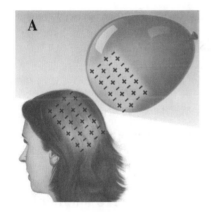

1. _____

2. _____

3. _____

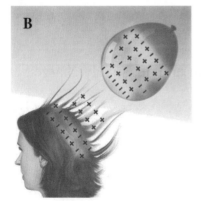

4. _____

5. _____

6. _____

3.2 Assessment

Match each description on the left with the term it best matches on the right. Each term may be used only once.

Description	Term
1. ____ positive charge	A. charging by friction
2. ____ negative charge	B. electron
3. ____ like charges repel each other	C. law of electric charge
4. ____ charging a material by rubbing	D. proton
5. ____ uncharged material	E. electrically neutral

Circle the letter of the best answer for questions 6 to 17.

6. What will happen if you rub two different materials together?

  A. They will always repel each other.

  B. They will always attract each other.

  C. Atoms may rub off one material and be transferred to the other.

  D. Electrons may rub off one material and be transferred to the other.

7. Why can protons not be rubbed off one material and transferred to another?

  A. They are part of the nucleus of atoms and are held firmly in place.

  B. They are part of the neutrons of atoms and are held firmly in place.

  C. They surround the nucleus and are tightly bound to it.

  D. They are too massive.

8. Which of the following is true of storm clouds?

  A. They are always positively charged at the bottom and negatively charged at the top.

  B. They can become charged by friction.

  C. They do not obey the law of electric charge.

  D. They are always electrically neutral.

9. What is always true of an object that is electrically neutral?

  A. It has more protons than electrons.

  B. It has more electrons than protons.

  C. It has an equal number of protons and electrons.

  D. It has no protons or electrons.

10. What is always true of an object that is electrically charged?

  A. It has more protons than electrons.

  B. It has more electrons than protons.

  C. It has an unequal number of protons and electrons.

  D. It has no protons or electrons.

11. Which of the following are true of materials with an equal number of positive and negative charges?

I	They are uncharged.
II	They have an equal number of protons and electrons.
III	They do not attract or repel each other.

  A. I and II only   **C.** II and III only

  B. I and III only   **D.** I, II, and III

12. You take a toque off your head in winter and your hair clings to it. Which of the following best explain what has occurred?

I	Both materials have become electrically neutral.
II	Both materials have become charged by friction.
III	Both materials attract each other.

  A. I and II only

  B. I and III only

  C. II and III only

  D. I, II, and III

13. You take the laundry out of the dryer and find your cotton socks stuck to your polar fleece vest. Which of the following are true of both materials?

I	Both materials have become electrically charged.
II	Both materials have an unequal number of charges.
III	Both materials are obeying the law of electric charge.

  A. I and II only   **C.** II and III only

  B. I and III only   **D.** I, II, and III

Use the image and text below to answer questions 14 and 15.

Experiments were performed with three balloons, labelled X, Y, and Z. The results of bringing two different pairs of balloons close together are shown below.

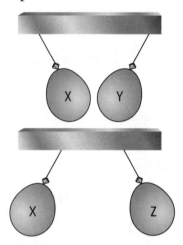

14. What can you infer about balloon X and balloon Y?

  A. Both must be charged.

  B. Both must be neutral.

  C. At least one of them must be charged.

  D. Nothing can be inferred.

15. What can you infer about balloon X and balloon Z?

  A. Both must be charged.

  B. Both must be neutral.

  C. At least one of them must be charged.

  D. Nothing can be inferred.

16. Which of the following are true of the law of electric charge?

I	Opposite charges attract each other.
II	Opposite charges repel each other.
III	Like charges repel each other.

   A. I and II only   **C.** II and III only

   B. I and III only   **D.** I, II, and III

17. The law of electric charge applies to all individual charges. Which of the following are true of a single negative charge as a result?

I	It repels all other negative charges.
II	It repels only the negative charges closest to it.
III	It attracts all other positive charges.

   A. I and II only

   B. I and III only

   C. II and III only

   D. I, II, and III

18. Complete the graphic organizer.

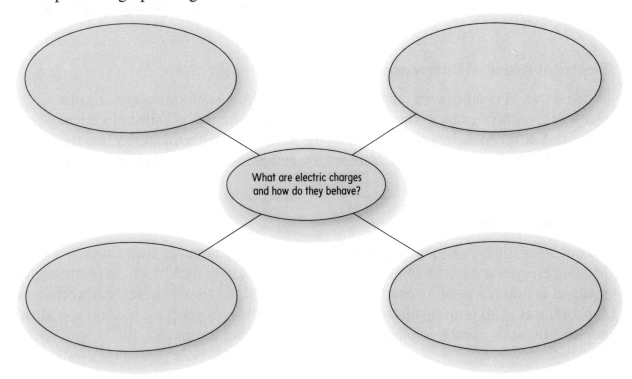

What are electric charges and how do they behave?

How do charges flow through the components of a circuit?

Use with textbook pages 212–227.

Cells and Batteries

A **source** is anything that supplies electrical energy. Cells and batteries are sources. A battery is a connection of two or more cells. In a cell, chemical reactions occur at sites called electrodes. Electrodes are made of metals which allow the flow of electrons through them. The electrodes sit in a solution called an electrolyte. The reactions cause one electrode to become positively charged, and the other to become negatively charged. The electrodes are in contact with terminals in the cell. When terminals are connected to an electrical pathway, charges flow through them.

There are two types of cells. A dry cell, such as an AA battery, contains a moist paste as an electrolyte. In a wet cell, the electrodes sit in a liquid solution. A car battery is an example of a wet cell. Review Figure 3.13 on page 214 of the textbook to compare these cells.

How a Cell Works

In a cell, chemical reactions separate positive and negative charges. Because work goes into separating the charges, the electrons now have the energy to do other work, like running a laptop. The energy stored in the cell is electrical potential energy. It has the potential to do work because of the separation or position of the charges. Review Figure 3.15 on page 215 of the textbook. How are positive and negative charges separated within a cell?

Electrical Potential Difference

When a unit of charge passes through a source, such as a cell or battery, it gains electrical potential energy. The quantity used to measure this is called **electrical potential difference**. It is determined by the nature of the chemical reaction that takes place in the cell. When cells are connected together in a battery, their electrical potential differences add up.

Conductivity and Current

A conductor is a type of material that allows electrical charges to flow through it. Moving charges are called an electric **current**. How easily the charges move through a material is referred to as its **conductivity**. A material through which electrical charges cannot travel at all is an **insulator**. Most metals, such as copper, are conductors. Most non-metals, such as rubber, plastic, glass, and wood, are insulators.

Resistance and Load

A device that converts electrical energy into another form of energy
is a **load**. Light bulbs and radios are examples of loads. A load
slows the flow of current. Study Figure 3.18 on page 220 of the textbook to review why
this happens. The degree to which the flow of current is hindered is called **resistance**.

Completing a Circuit

An **electrical circuit** forms when a source, load, and conductor are connected in a way
that allows current to flow. For the current to flow, a circuit must be closed (form a
closed loop). Study Figure 3.20 on page 222 of the textbook to see how current flows
through a simple, closed circuit. In a **short circuit** the current can get very high because
there is no load. The conductor can get hot enough to start a fire. If there is no closed
path along which current can flow, the circuit is called an open circuit. The figures
below show examples of how a circuit can be opened or closed with a switch.

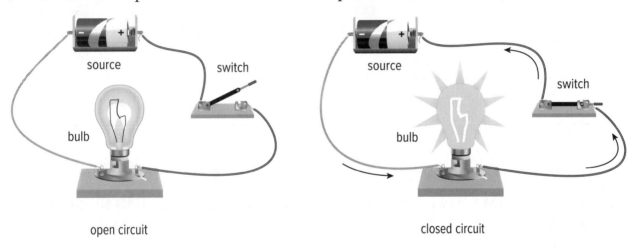

open circuit   closed circuit

Symbols, Units, and Circuit Diagrams

Symbols are used to make it easier to communicate what is happening in a circuit.

- Electrical potential difference has the symbol V and is measured in units called volts
  (V).

- Current has the symbol I and is measured in units called amperes (A).

- Resistance has the symbol R and is measured in units called ohms (Ω).

Circuits are also drawn using symbols. These drawings are called circuit diagrams.
Table 3.1 on page 223 of the textbook shows the different symbols used in these
diagrams. Review Figure 3.22 on the same page to see how they can be used to draw a
circuit.

The Terminology of a Circuit

Use with textbook pages 214–220.

1. Interpreting Key Terms

Words can have more than one meaning, depending on their context. The chart below shows some words that you may have seen in a non-scientific context. For each word, fill in its everyday meaning and its scientific meaning, specifically in the context of Topic 3.3. The first one has been done for you.

Word	Everyday Meaning	Scientific Meaning (Physics)
a) cell	small room in a prison	a small, portable source that transforms chemical energy into electrical energy
b) source		
c) current		
d) load		
e) resistance		

2. Knowing the everyday meaning of a word can also help you recall its scientific meaning. For each word above, explain how its everyday meaning is related to its scientific meaning.

a) cell _____

_____

b) source _____

_____

c) current _____

_____

d) load _____

_____

e) resistance _____

_____

The Flow of Current

Use with textbook pages 214-222.

1. Comparing and Contrasting—Using Tables

Comparing and contrasting new concepts can help you understand them. Venn diagrams and tables are two ways to organize this information graphically. The table below shows the differences and similarities between a series circuit and a parallel circuit.

Term	Similarities	Differences
series circuit	Both provide closed paths along which electrons can flow.	There is only one path along which electrons can flow.
parallel circuit		There is more than one path along which electrons can flow.

Complete a table like the one above for each of the following pairs of terms.

a) wet cell and dry cell

Term	Similarities	Differences

b) open circuit and closed circuit

Term	Similarities	Differences

c) conductor and insulator

Term	Similarities	Differences

Resistance Is Useful

Use with textbook page 220.

Use the panels on this page to create a comic about what happens to electrons as they travel through a light bulb filament to create light. The comic should include the following words at least once: resistance, load, collision(s), filament, current, electron(s), and atom(s).

Circuit Diagrams

Use with textbook pages 221–224.

1. Draw the circuit diagram symbol for each component given below.

  a) closed switch   **b)** conducting wire   **c)** cell

  d) open switch   **e)** battery   **f)** load

2. Use the circuit diagrams below to answer the questions that follow.

A 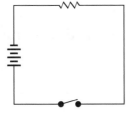   B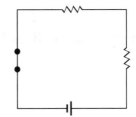

  a) In which circuit is current not flowing? Provide your reasoning.

  _____

  _____

  b) In which circuit is the source a battery? _____

  c) Which circuit has more loads? _____

  d) Which source most likely has a higher electrical potential difference? Explain.

  _____

  _____

3. a) Draw a circuit diagram for a closed circuit with a battery, a toy motor, a light bulb, and a switch.

b) What will happen to the light bulb if the toy motor breaks and stops running? Explain.

_____

_____

_____

_____

_____

Comparing an Electrical Circuit and a Water Circuit

Use with textbook page 224.

1. For each component of a water circuit below, describe its matching component in an electrical circuit.

   a) Water Circuit: The pump in a water circuit lifts water to a higher level against the pull of gravity.

   Electrical Circuit:

   _____

   _____

   _____

   b) Water Circuit: The valve on the pipe controls whether the water flows.

   Electrical Circuit:

   _____

   _____

   _____

   c) Water Circuit: The flow of water turns a water wheel.

   Electrical Circuit:

   _____

   _____

   _____

3.3 Assessment

Match each description on the left with the term it best matches on the right. Each term may be used only once.

Description	Term
1. _____ a fire hazard if it occurs within a building's wiring	A. short circuit
2. _____ must be closed for current to flow	B. load
3. _____ a cell, battery, or electrical outlet	C. conductivity
4. _____ units for electrical potential difference	D. electrical circuit
5. _____ can open or close a circuit	E. electrical potential energy
6. _____ how easily charges travel through a material	F. source
7. _____ a radio, light bulb, or oven	G. resistance
8. _____ stored in a cell	H. electrochemical cell
9. _____ measured in units called ohms	I. volts
10. _____ uses electrodes and an electrolyte to generate electrical energy	J. switch

Circle the letter of the best answer for questions 11 to 28.

11. Which of the following is true of a battery?

    A. It is an electrical potential cell.

    B. It is an electrochemical cell.

    C. It is two or more electrochemical cells linked together.

    D. None of the above.

12. Which of the following is true of an electrolyte?

    A. It is a component of a cell, but not a battery.

    B. It is a component of a wet cell but not a dry cell.

    C. It is a component of a dry cell but not a wet cell.

    D. It is a component of both a wet cell and a dry cell.

13. Which of the following is an example of a source?

    A. a light bulb   **C.** an electrical outlet

    B. a switch   **D.** an electrode

14. Because work went into separating charges in a cell, electrons in the cell now have

A. electrical potential energy.

C. a low resistance.

B. a high current.

D. chemical energy.

15. In an analogy in which a worker carries charges up a ladder to separate them in a cell, what does the worker represent?

A. potential energy

B. kinetic energy

C. chemical energy

D. mechanical energy

16. A battery is marked as 6 V. This is a measurement of which of the following?

I	current
II	voltage
III	electrical potential difference

A. I and II only

C. II and III only

B. I and III only

D. I, II, and III

17. Why does it take energy to separate positive and negative charges in a cell?

A. They are being separated against the force of gravity.

B. They are being separated against the force of chemical energy.

C. The opposite charges repel each other.

D. The opposite charges attract each other.

18. Which of the following is true of electrical potential difference?

A. It differs from voltage.

B. It represents the amount of energy that it took to separate the last unit of charge in a cell.

C. It is the same as current.

D. It represents the difference in resistance between the two terminals of a cell.

19. A unit of charge is also called a(n)

    A. volt.   **C.** coulomb.

    B. ampere.   **D.** electron.

20. Which of the following is an insulator?

    A. glass   **C.** silver

    B. aluminum   **D.** copper

21. Which of the following has the highest conductivity?

    A. a piece of wood   **C.** a plastic toy

    B. a rubber balloon   **D.** a stainless steel fork

22. The symbol I represents

    A. current.   **C.** resistance.

    B. electrical potential difference.   **D.** conductivity.

23. A device that converts electrical energy into another form of energy is a

    A. load.   **C.** insulator.

    B. resistor.   **D.** conductor.

24. Why can a short circuit be dangerous?

    A. The current can get so high that the conductor can get hot enough to start a fire.

    B. The voltage can get so high that the conductor can get hot enough to start a fire.

    C. The current can get so high that the insulator can get hot enough to start a fire.

    D. The voltage can get so high that the insulator can get hot enough to start a fire.

25. Which of the following is best described by the statement below?

As charges flow into the filament of a light bulb from a much larger wire, they collide with the surrounding atoms and the filament grows hot and glows.

    A. electrical potential difference

    B. insulator

    C. short circuit

    D. resistance

26. Which of the following are true of an electrical circuit?

I	It must be closed for current to flow.
II	It must be open for current to flow.
III	It requires a source for current to flow.

   A. I and II only

   B. I and III only

   C. II and III only

   D. I, II, and III

27. Which of the following pairs are matched correctly?

   A. volt – resistance

   B. ampere – resistance

   C. ohm – electrical potential difference

   D. ampere – current

28. An electrical circuit can be best compared to

   A. a one-way street.

   B. a water circuit.

   C. an escalator.

   D. a clock.

29. Complete the flowchart about the components of an electrical circuit.

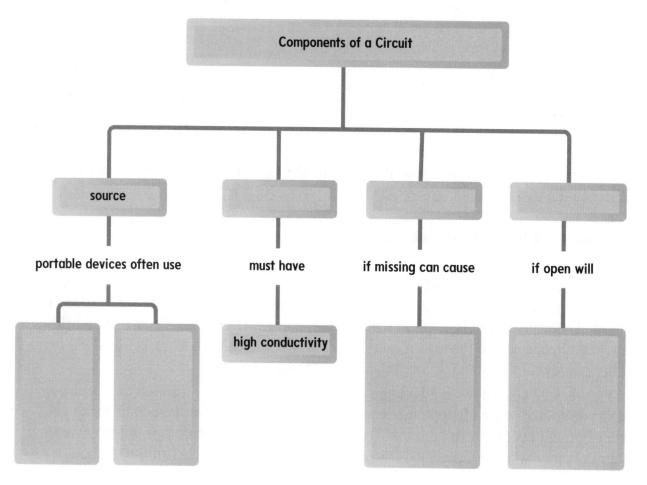

How are circuits used in practical applications?

Use with textbook pages 234–243.

Ohm's Law

Electrical potential difference, current, and resistance in a circuit are related by **Ohm's law**. Ohm's law states that the electrical potential difference between two points in a circuit is equal to the current multiplied by the resistance between those two points.

Ohm's law can be written as $V = IR$.

V is the symbol for electrical potential difference.

I is the symbol for current.

R is the symbol for resistance.

Series and Parallel Circuits

In a **series circuit**, current can only flow along one path. In a **parallel circuit**, there is at least one branch point where current splits into two or more pathways.

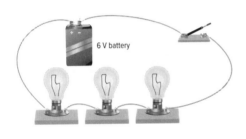

Series Circuit

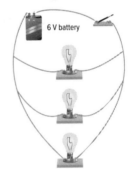

Parallel Circuit

Compare Figure 3.26 A and B on page 239 of the textbook. How do the flow of charges differ in the two circuits?

Practical Applications of Circuits

Appliances in a home are not wired in series because if one appliance in a series circuit stops working or is turned off, the circuit will open. As a result, current will no longer flow and none of the appliances will work. Instead, appliances in a home are wired in parallel. Because there is always an alternative pathway along which current can flow, each appliance can be turned off and on by its own switch without affecting the others. This is shown in Figure 3.27 on page 240 of the textbook.

Figure 3.27 also shows how a large amount of current passes through the conductor near the source when all appliances are running. This can cause the conductor to get very hot and become a fire hazard. To avoid this problem in buildings, many separate parallel circuits are installed, as shown in Figure 3.28 on page 241 of the textbook.

Series and Parallel Circuits

Use with textbook pages 221–223 and 238–239.

1. Understanding Analogies

An analogy is a comparison that highlights a likeness between two things that are otherwise unlike each other. Analogies can help you understand concepts by comparing something familiar to something unfamiliar. For instance, an analogy with a river can help you understand series and parallel circuits. As you read this analogy below, keep in mind that although there are some similarities between circuits and rivers, there are also many differences.

Some rivers have no branches. This type of river is similar to a series circuit. Just as the water current flows along just one path in the river, the electric current flows along just one path in a series circuit.

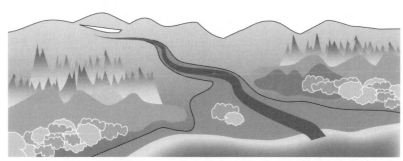

Other rivers have one or more branches. This type of river is similar to a parallel circuit. Just as the water current splits and flows along two or more pathways in the river, the electric current splits and flows along two or more pathways in a parallel circuit.

Come up with your own analogy to compare series and parallel circuits.

_____

_____

_____

_____

_____

Drawing Circuit Diagrams

Use with textbook pages 221–223 and 238–239.

Draw circuit diagrams in each space provided.

1. an open series circuit with a cell, switch, and fan

2. a closed parallel circuit with a battery and two light bulbs, each on its own branch

3. a closed series circuit with a battery and three loads in which current flows through the switch, the loads, and then back to the battery

Circuit Challenge

Use with textbook pages 221–223 and 238–239.

Use the text below to answer the questions that follow it.

Your teacher has set up an electrical circuit in the classroom. A cloth has been laid over all the components except for the loads: four light bulbs, each of a different colour. As a result, it is impossible to see how the circuit has been set up. Your teacher challenges you to draw a circuit diagram of the circuit. To help you determine how the circuit has been designed, your teacher performs the following tests.

Test A

Your teacher turns off the red light bulb. The blue light bulb turns off as well. The green and yellow light bulbs remain on.

Test B

Your teacher unscrews the green light bulb that remained on in test A. The yellow bulb immediately turns off. The other light bulbs remain on.

1. Draw a possible circuit diagram for the circuit. Label the light bulbs by colour.

2. Explain why you drew the circuit diagram as you did.

_____

_____

_____

_____

_____

Multiple Parallel Circuits

Use with textbook pages 240–241.

1. Interpreting Diagrams

A diagram is a simplified drawing that uses symbols to represent objects, directions, and relationships. The steps below can help you interpret a diagram.

Step 1: Read the text that introduces the diagram. This can help you understand the main idea of the diagram. It may also explain symbols used in the diagram.

Step 2: Read the title or caption. These may also help you understand the main idea of the diagram, especially if the introductory text did not. It often explains symbols as well.

Step 3: Finally, study the diagram itself. Apply what you learned in steps 1 and 2 to help you understand it.

Many separate parallel circuits are installed in buildings, as shown in Figure 1 below. A large electrical cable transports electrical energy from a power company to a building. This cable is connected to many parallel circuits inside a circuit panel. Each solid line leaving the circuit panel represents a single parallel circuit. The circuits leave the panel and transport electrical energy within the building.

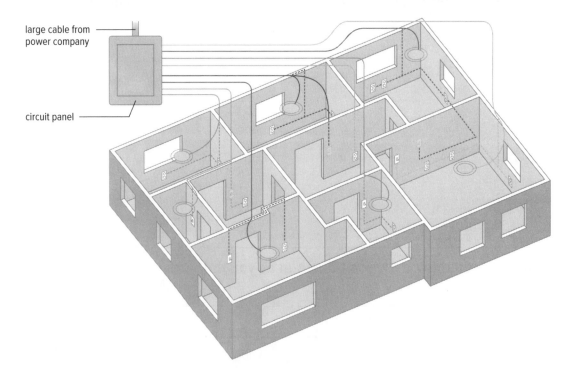

Figure 1 Buildings have multiple parallel circuits, as shown in this diagram. The disks represent ceiling lights.

---

a) What is the main idea of the diagram?

_____

_____

b) What information about the symbols used in the diagram is provided in the introductory text?

_____

_____

c) What information about symbols used in the diagram is provided in the caption?

_____

_____

d) How do labels help you understand the diagram?

_____

_____

_____

_____

e) Sometimes, certain aspects of a diagram are left for you to interpret. What questions do you have about the diagram that the text, caption, and diagram do not answer?

_____

_____

_____

_____

From Generating Station to Television

Use with textbook pages 240–241.

In the box below, draw a sketch that shows how electrical energy travels from a generating station to a television in a home. Add any labels that will help clarify your drawing. When you are done, write a caption that explains your drawing.

3.4 Assessment

Match each description on the left with the type of circuit it best matches on the right. Each type of circuit will be used more than once.

Description	Type of Circuit
1. _____ used in wiring for buildings	**A.** series circuit
2. _____ one pathway for current to flow along	**B.** parallel circuit
3. _____ no loads run if one load burns out or is turned off	
4. _____ multiple pathways for current to flow along	
5. _____ other loads run if one load burns out or is turned off	
6. _____ can become a fire hazard if it has many loads	

Circle the letter of the best answer for questions 7 to 15.

7. Which of the following best reflects Ohm's law?

   A. Voltage, current, and resistance are related.

   B. Voltage, electrical potential difference, and resistance are related.

   C. Voltage, current, and electrical potential difference are related.

   D. Voltage, current, and flow of charges are related.

8. Which equations correctly summarize Ohm's law?

I	$V = IR$
II	$R = \dfrac{V}{I}$
III	$R = VI$

   A. I and II only   **C.** II and III only

   B. I and III only   **D.** I, II, and III

9. What two pieces of information would you need to find the current flowing through your cellphone?

   A. the current provided by the battery and the electrical potential difference of the phone

   B. the current provided by the battery and the resistance of the phone

   C. the electrical potential difference of the phone and the resistance of the battery

   D. the electrical potential difference of the battery and the resistance of the phone

10. Which type of circuit is shown below?

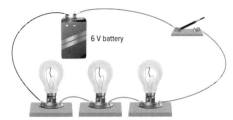

6 V battery

A. an open parallel circuit   **C.** an open series circuit

B. a closed parallel circuit   **D.** a closed series circuit

11. Which of the following is true at point A of the circuit below?

A. The current increases.

B. The current decreases.

C. The current alternates.

D. There is no current.

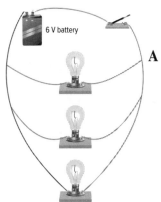

6 V battery

A

12. Which of the following is true of series circuits?

A. They are impractical for wiring a building.

B. They cannot carry enough current to run appliances.

C. They are unsafe to use in a building.

D. None of the above.

Use the following diagram to answer questions 13 to 15.

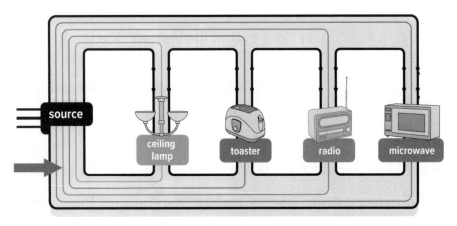

source — ceiling lamp — toaster — radio — microwave

13. What is represented by the diagram?

    A. a closed series circuit

    B. an open series circuit

    C. a closed parallel circuit

    D. an open parallel circuit

14. What would happen to the radio if the switch to the toaster were turned off?

    A. It would play louder.

    B. It would stop playing.

    C. It would play quieter.

    D. It would continue to play as before.

15. What is the arrow in the diagram most likely indicating?

    A. When all the appliances are off, a large amount of current is passing through the conductor near the source.

    B. When all the appliances are on, the amount of current passing through the conductor decreases near the source.

    C. When all the appliances are on, a large amount of current is passing through the conductor near the source.

    D. None of the above.

16. Complete the following concept map for a parallel circuit.

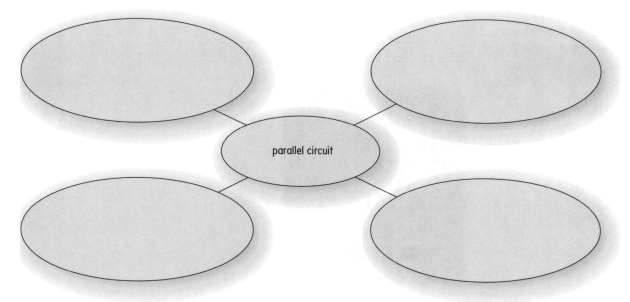

parallel circuit

How can electrical energy be generated and used sustainably?

Use with textbook pages 250–263.

Measuring Use of Electrical Energy

Watts and kilowatts are used to measure **electrical power**, the rate at which electrical energy is used by a load. Kilowatt-hours are used to measure the electrical energy used by a load over time. **Smart meters** measure how electrical energy use changes in a building over the course of the day.

Sustainable Use of Electrical Energy

Smart meters can encourage people to use electrical energy more sustainably by giving people a means to track how and when they use it. **EnerGuide labels** and **ENERGY STAR® labels** help consumers buy more energy-efficient appliances.

The large number shows how much energy the appliance uses in one year of normal use.

The shaded bar below the large number shows how the appliance compares with similar ones on the market.

The numbers on the bar give a range of efficiency for yearly energy use. The left end is the lowest (most efficient). The right end is the highest (least efficient).

Canada

ENERG**UIDE**

Energy consumption / Consommation énergétique

267 **kWh**
per year / par année
This model / Ce modèle

189 kWh   1000 kWh

Uses least energy /
Consomme le moins
d'énergie

Uses most energy /
Consomme le plus
d'énergie

Similar models
compared   **Standard / Ordinaire**   Modèles similaires
compared   comparés

Model number   Numéro du modèle

Removal of this label before first retail purchase is an offense (S.C. 1992 c/36)

Unplugging devices and appliances with **phantom loads** also reduces energy use. These devices use electrical energy even when they are turned off. The figure below shows a variety of devices with phantom loads.

Nonrenewable and Renewable Energy Sources

Nonrenewable energy sources cannot be replaced within a human lifetime. **Renewable energy sources** are produced on a continual basis or can be replenished fairly quickly. Fossil fuels and uranium are nonrenewable energy sources. Renewable energy sources include sunlight, wind, river flow, tides and waves, geothermal sources, and biomass. Both types of energy sources are used to generate electrical energy in B.C., as shown in Figure 3.33 on pages 258 and 259 of the textbook.

Using Electrical Energy Sustainably as a Society

Society has begun to see a need for a **sustainable energy system**. This involves perceiving, producing, and using all energy more sustainably. Many characteristics of a sustainable energy system are similar to the principles of First Peoples Ecosystem Based Management (EBM). These principles focus on respect and responsibility, intergenerational knowledge, balance and interconnectedness, and giving and receiving.

Using Electrical Energy Sustainably

Use with textbook pages 254–257.

1. Comparing and Contrasting—Using Graphic Organizers

Comparing and contrasting can help you identify how concepts are similar or different. A Venn diagram can help you organize this information graphically. Complete the following Venn diagrams to show some of the similarities and differences between the given concepts.

a)

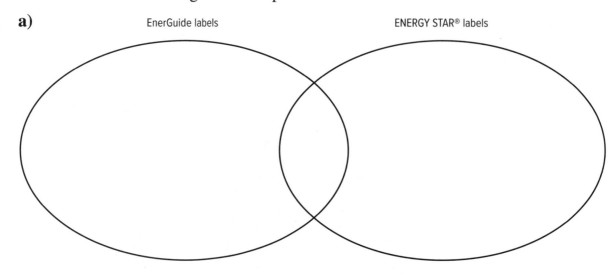

EnerGuide labels   ENERGY STAR® labels

b)

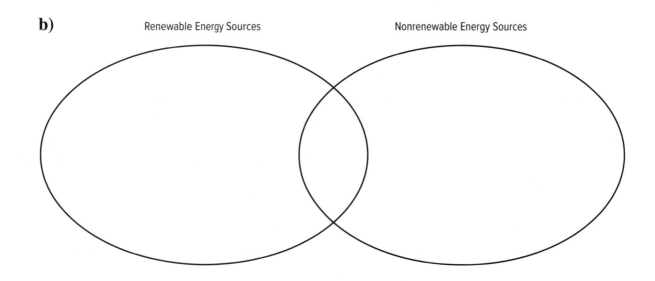

Renewable Energy Sources   Nonrenewable Energy Sources

Deciphering "Nonrenewable"

Use with textbook page 257.

1. **Using Base Words**

   One strategy that can help you understand the meaning of a new word is to cut it down to its base. For example, follow the steps below to figure out the meaning of the word *unobtainable*.

   Step 1: Cut the word down to its base: obtain. This means *to get*.

   Step 2: Build the word back up from the base by adding the ending: *-able* changes the meaning of the word to mean *able to get*.

   Step 3: Finally, add the beginning of the word: *-un* means not. From here you can figure out that unobtainable means *not able to get*.

   Follow the steps above to predict the meaning of *nonrenewable*. Then check your predictions against the meaning of the term in the textbook on page 257.

   _____

   _____

   _____

   _____

   _____

   _____

Electrical Power and Electrical Energy

Use with textbook pages 252–256.

1. Explain how the terms electrical power and electrical energy are similar, and how they are different.

_____

_____

_____

_____

2. Make and explain connections between the terms below. Make as many connections as possible. Think about how these terms relate to electrical power or electrical energy to help you.

kilowatt-hours (kWh)	energy-efficient
power rating	smart meters
watts (W)	phantom loads

_____

_____

_____

_____

_____

_____

_____

_____

_____

_____

_____

_____

_____

Fight the Phantom Advertising Campaign

Use with textbook pages 254–256.

Imagine you are working for an advertising agency. Your employer has asked you to write a script for a radio advertisement about phantom loads. The advertisement is part of a national campaign to educate Canadians about using electrical energy more sustainably. This includes reducing phantom loads in their home or workplace. Your advertisement must reflect the theme "Fight the Phantom," but it can use any format you like.

_____

_____

_____

_____

_____

_____

_____

_____

_____

_____

_____

_____

_____

_____

_____

_____

_____

_____

_____

_____

_____

_____

_____

_____

Generation Road Trip

Use with textbook pages 258–259.

Plan a road trip to visit four locations that generate (or have the potential to generate) electrical energy in B.C. For each stop, identify the location, state how it generates electrical energy, and explain why you chose to visit it.

Stop 1:

_____

_____

_____

_____

_____

Stop 2:

_____

_____

_____

_____

_____

Stop 3:

_____

_____

_____

_____

_____

Stop 4:

_____

_____

_____

_____

_____

Sustainable Use of Electrical Energy

Use with textbook pages 252–261.

Complete the PMI chart below for the sustainable use of electrical energy.

Plus	Minus	Interesting

3.5 Assessment

Match each description on the left with the term it best matches on the right. Each term may be used only once.

Description	Term
1. ____ measures how electrical energy use changes in a building	A. kilowatt-hours
2. ____ electrical energy that a device uses when it is turned off	B. power rating
3. ____ tells you a product meets standards for energy efficiency	C. ENERGY STAR® label
4. ____ the unit used to measure the amount of energy used by an appliance	D. EnerGuide label
5. ____ the rate at which an appliance uses energy	E. phantom load
6. ____ tells you the amount of energy an appliance uses in one year	F. smart meter

Circle the letter of the best answer for questions 7 to 22.

7. Which of the following are true of 1000 W?

I	It equals 1 kW.
II	It is a rate.
III	It could be the power rating of an appliance.

   A. I and II only

   B. I and III only

   C. II and III only

   D. I, II, and III

8. Electrical power is measured in

   A. amperes.

   B. watts.

   C. kilowatt-hours.

   D. volts.

9. If you run a 5000 W clothes dryer for 1 hour, how many kilowatt-hours (kWh) have you used?

   A. 5000 kWh

   B. 500 kWh

   C. 50 kWh

   D. 5 kWh

10. Which of the following is true of a smart meter?

   A. It measures changes in the use of electrical power.

   B. It measures changes in the use of electrical energy.

   C. It sends data to the utility company through large underground cables.

   D. It sends signals to the utility company once a week.

11. Which tools can help people use electrical energy more sustainably?

   A. smart meters

   B. ENERGY STAR® labels

   C. EnerGuide labels

   D. All of the above.

12. Which label indicates that an appliance uses 10 to 50 percent less energy compared with a standard appliance in the same category?

   A. power rating label

   B. EnerGuide label

   C. ENERGY STAR® label

   D. phantom load label

13. What is a phantom load?

   A. the electrical energy a device uses when it is turned off

   B. the hidden electrical power drain of all appliances

   C. an energy source with no impact on the environment

   D. a load you cannot see, like under the floor heating

14. Which of the following are true of nonrenewable energy sources?

I	They include river flow and tides.
II	They are not sustainable.
III	They are not renewable in a human lifetime.

   A. I and II only   **C.** II and III only

   B. I and III only   **D.** I, II, and III

Read the text below. Then answer questions 15 to 18.

A school camp is being built in a remote area. The school board is deciding what energy source to use to generate electrical energy. The options they are considering include

I	natural gas to run a generator system
II	sunlight for photovoltaic cells
III	wind to turn a wind turbine
IV	diesel to run a generator system

15. Which of the options use a nonrenewable energy source?

   A. I and IV only   **C.** II and III only

   B. I and II only   **D.** II and IV only

16. Which of the options use a renewable energy source?

   A. I and II only   **C.** II and III only

   B. I and IV only   **D.** III and IV only

17. Which of the options has been used successfully at Kitasoo Community School?

   A. I   **C.** III

   B. II   **D.** IV

18. Which of the options has been used successfully at Bear Mountain in northern British Columbia?

   A. I   **C.** III

   B. II   **D.** IV

19. What is true of renewable energy sources?

   A. They are unlikely to be used up in a human lifetime.

   B. They provide sustainable options for generating electrical energy.

   C. They are often produced on a continual basis.

   D. All of the above.

20. How does the Race Rocks Tidal Energy Project generate electrical energy?

    A. It transforms the kinetic energy of high and low tides into electrical energy.

    B. It transforms the kinetic energy of tidal currents into electrical energy.

    C. It transforms the kinetic energy of waves into electrical energy.

    D. All of the above.

21. At SunMine, 4000 photovoltaic cells are mounted on 96 solar trackers. Which of the following best explains the function of the trackers?

    A. They follow the Sun's movement through the sky over the course of the day.

    B. They reflect sunlight to increase the amount of electrical energy generated.

    C. They hold down the photovoltaic cells during strong winds on the mountain.

    D. They lift the photovoltaic cells so that they are closer to the Sun.

22. Which of the following are characteristics of a sustainable energy system?

I	less reliance on decreasing nonrenewable energy sources
II	consideration of current and future generations
III	consideration of Earth's entire population

    A. I and II only   **C.** II and III only

    B. I and III only   **D.** I, II, and III

23. Complete the fishbone diagram below for the principles of First Peoples Ecosystem Based Management. Two principles and details have been completed for you.

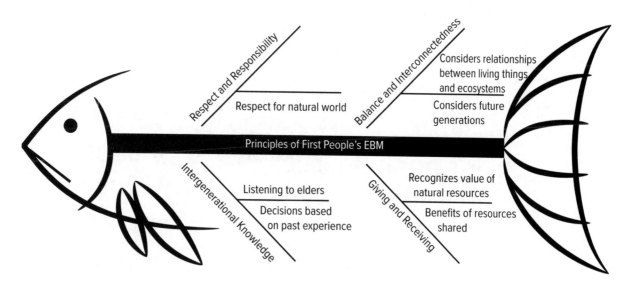

Can small-scale changes make a big impact on energy sustainability?

What's the Issue?

Headlines such as the ones below indicate that the world is moving toward a sustainable energy system. But while these headlines reveal a large-scale shift toward such a system, change is taking place on a small scale as well. A movement is occurring in garages and workshops, in laboratories and classrooms, and on computers and tablets around the world. People, from students and hobbyists to professional engineers, are creating a variety of technologies that use renewable energy sources. Some are practical gadgets that help accomplish a task, such as charging a cellphone or getting around town. Others are fun novelties, like toys and games. Whatever they do, these technologies all support the change to a sustainable energy system.

Wind Power Potential:
China Builds Two Wind Turbines Each Hour

Iceland Digs Deep:
World's Hottest Geothermal Source to Be Developed

Renewable Sources Are New Leader in Global Electrical Energy Race

Dig Deeper

Collaborate with your classmates to explore one or more of these questions—or generate your own questions to explore.

1. Ann Makosinski was a high school student in B.C. when she designed a coffee mug that transforms thermal energy from a hot beverage to electrical energy. This electrical energy is used to charge a cellphone. The young inventor was invited to appear on television's *The Tonight Show* as a result. If you were the host of the show, what questions would you have for Ann Makosinski?

2. Human-produced energy can help generate electrical energy to run devices in remote or poor locations. For example, the One Laptop Per Child project provides school children in developing countries with laptop computers. The students generate electrical energy to run the computers by turning a hand crank. How is this project in line with the characteristics of a sustainable energy system?

3. Chinese farmer Tang Zhengping built a wind-powered car, despite the fact that he had no engineering background at all. Research another example of how vehicles are taking advantage of renewable energy sources to support a sustainable energy system. (Think not just road transportation, but sky and sea as well.)

4. From a solar-powered cockroach to a wind-powered robot—some of the most unique and innovative toys on the market use renewable energy sources. Find out more about a toy that uses a renewable energy source that interests you. What questions do you have about it? How can you find the answers?

5. Investigate how your community (it could be your household, school, or broader community) is trying to reduce electrical energy use to become more sustainable.

How do the ideas of connection and sustainability help us think about Earth's spheres?

Use with textbook pages 282–291.

Everything Is Connected

The idea of interconnectedness is at the heart of what it is to be First Peoples. It is also at the heart of the modern environmental movement. Interconnectedness is the idea that all living and non-living parts of the environment are connected and the interaction of these parts affects both living and non-living things in any given environment.

The **biotic** parts of the environment include all living things. The **abiotic** parts of the environment are all of the non-living things. The biotic and abiotic parts of the environment are interconnected because they are constantly interacting. For example, all living things use gases from the atmosphere, such as oxygen and carbon dioxide, to survive. As well, all living things need water to survive. The figure below shows the abiotic and biotic parts of the environment. How do the biotic and abiotic parts interact?

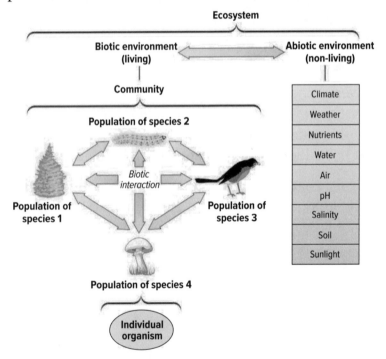

Earth's spheres consist of the atmosphere, geosphere, hydrosphere, and biosphere. Earth's spheres are also interconnected. Consider how rain interacts with all of Earth's spheres. Rain forms in the atmosphere and falls to Earth's surface as water that enters the hydrosphere. The water interacts with the geosphere when it soaks into soil, and with the biosphere when plant roots absorb it. Figure 4.4 on page 287 in the textbook shows more examples of how Earth's spheres are interconnected. Can you think of some other examples?

Ecosystem Services

Ecosystem services are the benefits that organisms receive from the environment and its resources. If ecosystems become unsustainable and break down, they no longer provide ecosystem services. Fossil fuels, timber, and minerals are examples of the raw materials ecosystem service. The table below shows a complete list of ecosystem services and examples of each.

Ecosystem Service	Example
Atmospheric gas supply	Regulation of carbon dioxide and oxygen
Climate regulation	Regulation of greenhouse gases
Cultural benefits	Aesthetic, spiritual, and educational value
Disturbance regulation	Storm protection, flood control, drought recovery, and other aspects of environmental response to disturbances
Food production	Crops, livestock, fish
Habitat (living space)	Habitat for migratory species and for locally harvested species, overwintering grounds, nurseries
Nutrient recycling	Carbon, nitrogen, and other nutrient cycles
Raw materials (natural resources)	Fossil fuels, timber, minerals
Soil erosion control	Retention of topsoil
Water supply	Supplying of water by reservoirs, watersheds, and wells

Scientific Literacy

Part of being scientifically literate is being able to tell fact from opinion and detect bias when reading, listening to, or discussing issues related to science. Bias is a judgment that is based on a person's knowledge, understanding, or beliefs. It is important to be able to recognize bias and understand how it may influence what you think about an idea or an issue. Refer to Table 4.2 on page 293 in the textbook for a list of critical thinking skills and questions you can ask to be scientifically literate.

Interconnectedness

Use with textbook pages 284–288.

Use the following reading passage, which is based on studies completed by Dr. Tom Reimchen of the University of Victoria to answer questions 1 and 2.

Salmon are hatched in freshwater streams throughout the temperate rainforest. They then migrate to the Pacific Ocean and spend their adult lives in the marine ecosystem. Every year, thousands of salmon swim upstream to return to the streams in which they hatched to spawn (reproduce). During this time, bears and other organisms, including wolves, bald eagles, and crows, feed on the salmon. In particular, bears move the salmon from the stream beds far into the forest. When the remains of the salmon decay in the forest, nutrients from their bodies, including nitrogen, enter the soil. Based on his research, Dr. Reimchen estimates that up to 70 percent of the nitrogen in plants, trees, insects, birds, and bears in the temperate rainforest comes from the Pacific Ocean via the salmon.

1. **Sequencing—Using Graphic Organizers**

    Complete the flowchart to sequence the events in the passage that show the connection between two ecosystems.

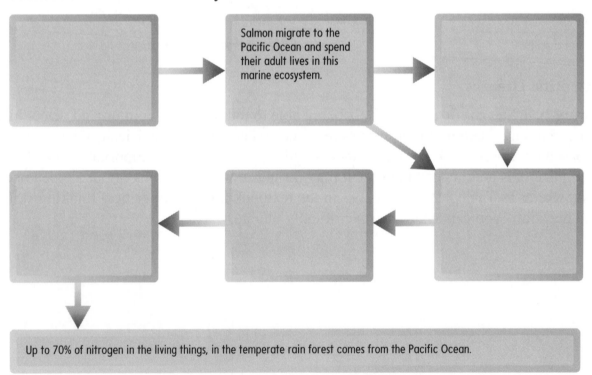

Salmon migrate to the Pacific Ocean and spend their adult lives in this marine ecosystem.

Up to 70% of nitrogen in the living things, in the temperate rain forest comes from the Pacific Ocean.

2. How should this research affect human decision making about spawning streams?

    _____

    _____

Connecting the Abiotic and Biotic Parts of the Environment

Use with textbook pages 286–287.

1. For each scenario in the table below, identify the abiotic part(s) and the biotic part(s).

Scenario	Abiotic Part(s)	Biotic Part(s)
A moose drinks water from a river.		
Heavy rains and landslides cause plants to be uprooted.		
Strong winds break branches off trees.		
A lack of nutrients in soil results in tomato plants not producing tomatoes.		
Plants that need shade are planted in an area that gets lots of sunlight. The leaves turn brown and the plants do not produce flowers.		
The pH of the water in an aquarium is too high and several fish die.		
Runoff from a heavy snowmelt reduces the salinity of the water in an estuary. Some of the reeds die and some of the fish leave the estuary for an area of higher salinity in the ocean.		

2. Give two new examples (not already given in your textbook) of how two of Earth's spheres interact.

a) The two spheres that interact are the _____ and the

_____.

b) They interact in the following way:

_____

_____

_____

c) The two spheres that interact are the _____ and the

_____.

d) They interact in the following way:

_____

_____

_____

Ecosystem Services

Use with textbook page 289.

1. For each ecosystem service listed in the table, answer the questions at the top of each column in the table. One row has been completed for you as an example.

Ecosystem Service	How do you benefit from this ecosystem service?	What question do you have about the ecosystem service?	How would you test your question in an investigation?
Cultural benefits			
Disturbance regulation			
Food production	I eat food every day.	What would happen if the supply of apples decreased?	I would look for past data of when apple crops were low due to weather or other factors. I would look for correlations between decreased apple supplies and the prices of apples, if imports of apples increased, and if the prices of any other foods were affected by the change in apple supply.
Water supply			

Recognizing Bias

Use with textbook pages 289–290.

1. Summarizing

Summarizing means restating the main ideas of a passage in your own words. A summary may be a sentence or paragraph, a series of bullet points, or an illustration or diagram. For example, the table below shows how to create a summary of the first paragraph on page 289 in the textbook.

Section of Text	Main Topic	What the Text Says about the Main Topic	Supporting Details
page 289, first paragraph	Natural ecosystems are sustainable.	1. Natural ecosystems can exist indefinitely as long as they have a continued and constant source of energy. 2. Natural ecosystems are always changing.	1. The system itself is always sustainable. 2. What is sustainable for some organisms at some times may not sustainable for them at other times.
Summary sentence: Natural ecosystems may change continually, but as long as they have a constant source of energy, they are sustainable.			

Read the paragraph on page 290 in the textbook and complete the table.

Section of Text	Main Topic	What the Text Says about the Main Topic	Supporting Details
Summary sentence:			

4.1 Assessment

Match each description on the left with the part of the environment on the right. Each part of the environment may be used more than once.

Description	Part of the Environment
1. ____ A bird builds a nest in the tree.	**A.** abiotic
2. ____ Increased carbon dioxide in the atmosphere causes the pH of ocean water to decrease.	**B.** biotic
3. ____ A caterpillar eats the leaves of a plant.	
4. ____ It rained four out of seven days last week.	
5. ____ In Location A, it is sunny and hot in the summer and cold with lots of snow in the winter.	
6. ____ A mushroom decomposes a fallen tree branch.	

Match each description on the left with the ecosystem service on the right. Each ecosystem service may be used only once.

Description	Ecosystem Service
7. ____ carbon, nitrogen, and other cycles	**A.** atmospheric gas supply
8. ____ regulation of carbon dioxide and oxygen	**B.** climate regulation
9. ____ homes for migratory species and nurseries	**C.** food production
10. ____ regulation of greenhouse gases	**D.** habitat (living space)
11. ____ fossil fuels, timber, minerals	**E.** nutrient recycling
12. ____ crops, livestock, fish	**F.** raw materials (natural resources)
13. ____ preventing the loss of topsoil	**G.** cultural benefits
14. ____ learning from and enjoying nature	**H.** water supply
15. ____ having sufficient drinking water	I soil erosion control

Circle the letter of the best answer for questions 16 to 26.

16. The solid, mainly rocky part of Earth is the

    A. atmosphere.

    B. biosphere.

    C. geosphere.

    D. hydrosphere.

17. Canadian Inuit leader Sheila Watt-Cloutier said, "We must now speak environment, economy, foreign policy, health, and human rights in the same breath. Everything is connected." The quote refers to the idea of

A. Earth's spheres.

B. ecosystem services.

C. interconnectedness.

D. science literacy.

18. Landslides cause trees to be uprooted and can destroy houses. Which two of Earth's spheres are interacting in this scenario?

A. atmosphere and geosphere

B. biosphere and geosphere

C. biosphere and hydrosphere

D. hydrosphere and atmosphere

19. Which statement about water is true?

A. Water is found in all of Earth's spheres.

B. Water is found only in the hydrosphere.

C. Water is found only in the atmosphere and hydrosphere.

D. Water is found only in the geosphere and hydrosphere.

20. When natural ecosystems are able to continue to exist indefinitely by recycling their materials as long as they have a continued and constant source of energy, they are

A. expendable.

B. replaceable.

C. sustainable.

D. unbalanced.

21. Ecosystem services are

A. all of the non-living parts of the environment.

B. all of the areas on Earth that are inhabited by and support life.

C. the result of ecosystems becoming unbalanced and unsustainable.

D. the benefits that organisms receive from the environment and its resources.

22. Which of the following are correct statements about ecosystem services?

I	Humans depend on them.
II	They are linked on a global scale.
III	If one ecosystem service fails, another will replace it.

A I and II only

B. I and III only

C. II and III

D. I, II, and III

23. Which is a judgment based on a person's knowledge, understanding, and beliefs?

A. bias

B. biotic parts

C. ecosystem services

D. interconnectedness

24. Which of the following is **not** an example of something to consider when you are trying to detect bias.

A. What makes the expert qualified in this issue?

B. The basic beliefs, attitudes, and values of the person or group presenting the information.

C. Whether you agree with the argument that is presented.

D. The evidence presented.

25. Which statement indicates a bias?

A. As of March 2017, the world population was 7.45 billion people.

B. The population of Canada is about 36 million people.

C. The world's population is too large and is putting a strain on natural resources.

D. In 2016, 16.4% of all electricity on Earth was generated by hydropower.

26. Which statement(s) indicate a bias about Earth Day?

A. Earth Day is the best day of the year, it is so important to observe it.

B. Earth Day is ridiculous, and no one should waste time observing it.

C. Neither statement A or B.

D. Both statements A and B.

27. Read the passage below. Then, draw a diagram to show how the resources mentioned in the passage are interconnected.

Both avalanche lily and balsamroot, as well as other food resources, depended upon the harvesting, processing, and preparation of a number of resources. These included the woods used for making the digging sticks; the birch bark, red-cedar root, and cherry bark for the baskets needed to transport the roots; the maple bark used to string the bulbs or roots for drying; the Indian hemp fiber, silverberry, or other fibers used for weaving storage bags; and the fuel and vegetation used for cooking and flavoring them. (Turner 1996, 1997a, 1998)

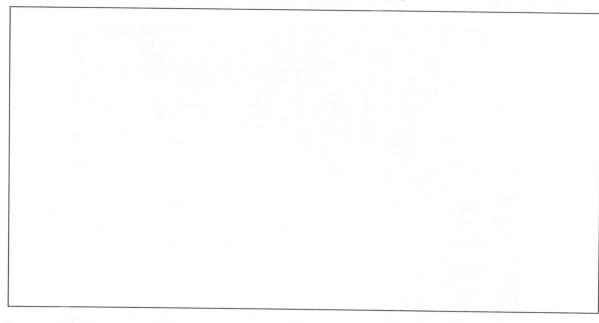

28. Draw a diagram to show how the ecosystem services of water supply and food production are interconnected.

What is the role of the Sun's energy in Earth's spheres?

Use with textbook pages 296–305.

Solar Energy and the Greenhouse Effect

The figure below shows that the solar energy that reaches Earth is absorbed and reflected by Earth's atmosphere and Earth's surface. The process that absorbs outgoing solar energy in Earth's atmosphere is the **greenhouse effect**. The greenhouse effect moderates Earth's temperature. Average global temperature would be –18 °C if greenhouse gases were not naturally found in the atmosphere.

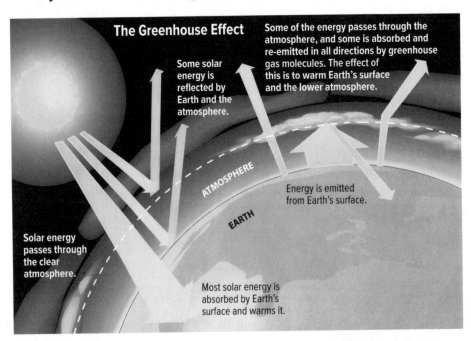

The Greenhouse Effect

Some solar energy is reflected by Earth and the atmosphere.

Some of the energy passes through the atmosphere, and some is absorbed and re-emitted in all directions by greenhouse gas molecules. The effect of this is to warm Earth's surface and the lower atmosphere.

ATMOSPHERE

EARTH

Energy is emitted from Earth's surface.

Solar energy passes through the clear atmosphere.

Most solar energy is absorbed by Earth's surface and warms it.

Greenhouse gases are gases that absorb solar energy in Earth's atmosphere. They include water vapour, carbon dioxide, methane, and nitrous oxide. The natural sources of greenhouse gases are listed in Table 4.3 on page 299 in the textbook. Greenhouses gases can also be released into the atmosphere as a result of human activities.

The Sun Heats Earth Unevenly, Creating Wind

Solar energy heats Earth's surface unevenly because Earth is spherical. Figure 4.8 on page 300 in the textbook shows that solar energy strikes Earth's curved surface at different angles. As a result, the atmosphere heats up unevenly and wind is created. Global wind systems, including the trade winds, the westerlies, and the polar easterlies, move thermal energy around Earth. Figure 4.9 on page 301 in the textbook shows the location and direction of the different wind systems. Which system affects the weather in B.C.?

Ocean Currents Redistribute Thermal Energy Around Earth

Ocean surface currents are created by wind. As shown in Figure 4.10 on page 302 in the textbook, there are five major sets of ocean currents. Poleward-flowing currents carry warm, tropical water into higher, colder latitudes. After these warm waters enter polar regions, they gradually cool. Currents that flow toward the equator bring cold water from higher latitudes to tropical regions. Deep-water currents are created when cold, dense water or salty, dense water at the surface sinks. The great ocean conveyor belt, shown below, carries water, heat, and nutrients around Earth. The black line represents cold water and the grey line represents warm water.

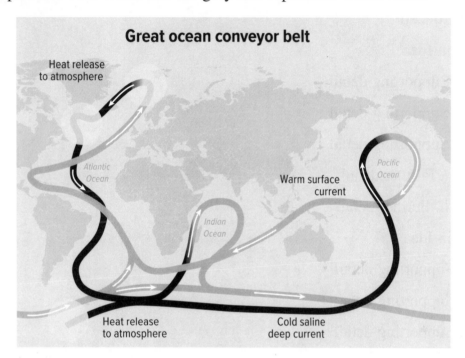

Great ocean conveyor belt

Photosynthesis and Cellular Respiration Are Complementary Processes

Green plants and certain kinds of single-celled organisms carry out photosynthesis. During photosynthesis, carbon dioxide and water are changed into glucose and oxygen, using light energy from the Sun. The chemical energy stored in glucose is converted to other forms of energy, such as kinetic energy and heat, during cellular respiration. Cellular respiration changes oxygen and glucose into carbon dioxide, water, and usable energy. Nearly all living things carry out cellular respiration.

The materials produced by photosynthesis are the materials used in cellular respiration and the materials produced by cellular respiration are used in photosynthesis. Together, both processes sustain life. Refer to Table 4.4 on page 304 in the textbook for a comparison of photosynthesis and cellular respiration.

Solar Energy and Earth's Atmosphere

Use with textbook page 298.

1. Outlining

Making an outline can help you organize the information you are reading and is a way of taking notes. Outlines usually follow a format that is similar to the example shown below.

I. Main Concept

   A. Main Idea

      1. Supporting detail

      2. Supporting detail

      3. Supporting detail

         i. Further detail

         ii. Further detail

   B. Main Idea

      1. Supporting detail

      2. Supporting detail

      3. Supporting detail

Use the format above to outline the information on page 298 in the textbook about what happens to solar energy when it enters Earth's atmosphere.

I. Solar energy reaches Earth's atmosphere.

   A. _____

      1. _____

         _____

      2. _____

         _____

      3. _____

         _____

         i. _____

         ii. _____

Global Winds and Ocean Currents

Use with textbook pages 301–302.

Use the diagram of Earth's wind systems to answer questions 1 to 4.

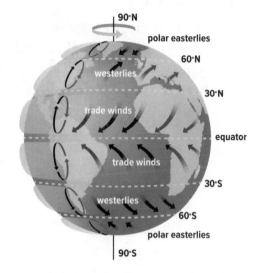

1. In which direction do the trade winds move?

_____

2. What happens to air as it approaches the equator?

_____

_____

_____

_____

_____

3. Which winds affect weather in much of North America? _____

4. Which winds are responsible for moving cold air from the poles toward the equator?

_____

5. Use the terms in the box to fill in the blanks in the paragraph below. Some terms may be used more than once.

cold	cool	landmass
warm	westerly	winds

Ocean surface currents are created by _____. In all ocean basins, warm water

currents near the equator flow in a _____ direction. When these currents reach a

_____, they turn toward the poles. These poleward-flowing waters carry

_____, tropical water into high colder latitudes. After these warm waters enter

polar regions, they gradually _____. Eventually, they reach a _____ and

begin flowing toward the equator. The resulting currents bring _____ water from

higher latitudes to tropical regions.

Ocean Currents

Use with textbook page 303.

1. Cause and Effect

Non-fiction text sometimes explains why something happens (the cause), or what happens as a result of something (the effect). You can use cause and effect boxes to identify a cause and its effect. For each cause that is listed, fill in the corresponding effect. For each effect that is listed, fill in the cause.

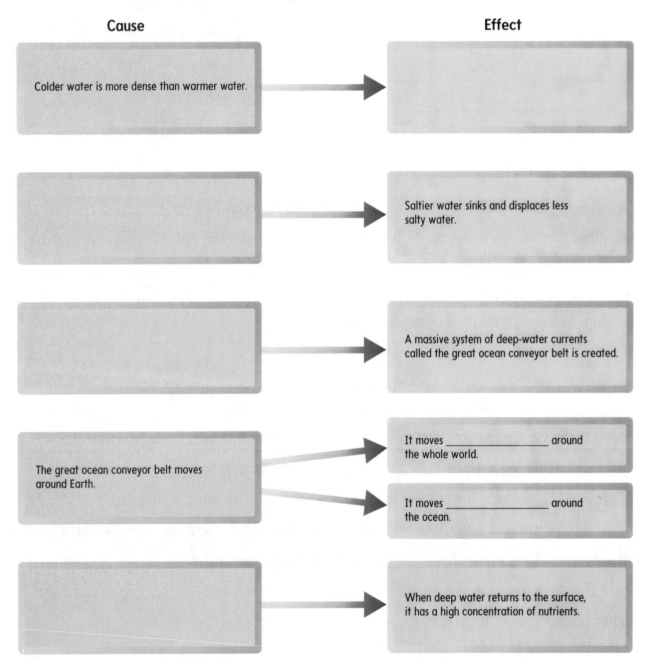

Cause | Effect

Colder water is more dense than warmer water. →

→ Saltier water sinks and displaces less salty water.

→ A massive system of deep-water currents called the great ocean conveyor belt is created.

The great ocean conveyor belt moves around Earth. →

It moves _____ around the whole world.

It moves _____ around the ocean.

→ When deep water returns to the surface, it has a high concentration of nutrients.

Photosynthesis and Cellular Respiration

Use with textbook pages 304–305.

1. The illustration shows the relationship between photosynthesis and cellular respiration. Use the terms in the box to fill in the labels on the illustration. More than one term can go on each blank line.

carbon dioxide	glucose	light energy
water	oxygen	usable energy

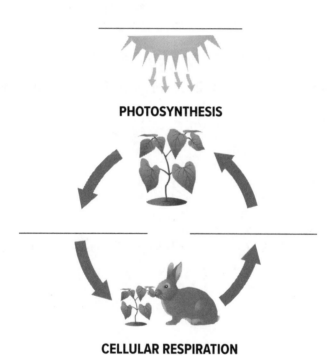

PHOTOSYNTHESIS

CELLULAR RESPIRATION

2. Suppose you have to explain that photosynthesis and cellular respiration are considered complementary processes to a group of grade 6 students. How could you use the illustration above as part of your explanation?

_____

_____

_____

_____

4.2 Assessment

Match each description with the type of prevailing wind. Each type of wind may be used more than once.

Description	Type of Prevailing Wind
1. _____ move from west to east and occur between 30°N and 60°N and 30°S and 60°S latitudes	**A.** trade winds
2. _____ move cold air from polar regions back toward the equator	**B.** westerlies
3. _____ created when air near the equator warms, rises, and travels to 30° north or south latitude	**C.** polar easterlies
4. _____ move much of the weather across parts of North America	
5. _____ move from east to west and occur between 60°N and 90°N and 60°S and 90°S latitudes	
6. _____ move from east to west and occur between the equator and 30°N and 30°S	

Circle the letter of the best answer for questions 7 to 20.

7. Which process absorbs outgoing solar energy in Earth's atmosphere?

   A. cellular respiration

   B. convection

   C. greenhouse effect

   D. photosynthesis

8. Which greenhouse gas enters Earth's atmosphere when fertilizer is applied to agricultural crops?

   A. carbon dioxide

   B. methane

   C. nitrous oxide

   D. water vapour

9. What happens to most of the solar energy that enters Earth's atmosphere?

   A. It is absorbed by land and water on Earth's surface.

   B. It is reflected by Earth's surface and atmosphere and passes through the atmosphere back into space.

   C. It is absorbed by gases in the atmosphere and re-emitted in all directions.

   D. It is re-emitted by Earth's surface and passes through the atmosphere back into space.

Use the table below to answer questions 10 to 12. Note that each numbered portion of the table is referred to as a cell.

Greenhouse Gas	Sources	Other Details
Water vapour	1	2
Carbon dioxide	3	• second most abundant greenhouse gas • produced in and by cells through cellular respiration
4	• certain species of bacteria and other micro-organisms that live in and around bogs, wetlands, melting permafrost • certain species of bacteria the live in the gut of animals such as cows and termites • vents and other openings in Earth's crust on land and the ocean floor	5
Nitrous oxide	6	• produced when certain species of bacteria break down nitrogen-rich compounds for food

10. Which of the following sources of greenhouse gas is the most appropriate to place in cell 1 of the table?

A. bacteria that live in oceans and wet, warm soils such as those in the tropics

B. evaporation from water

C. vents and other openings in Earth's crust on land and the ocean floor

D. volcanoes, forest fires, decaying organisms, release from oceans

11. Which of the following sources of greenhouse gas is the most appropriate to place in cell 3 of the table?

A. evaporation from water

B. living organisms

C. certain species of bacteria that live in the gut of animals such as cows and termites

D. bacteria that live in oceans and wet, warm soils such as those in the tropics

12. Which of the following details is the most appropriate to place in cell 5 of the table?

A. most abundant greenhouse gas

B. produced during cellular respiration and certain plant processes

C. produced by plants during photosynthesis

D. a by-product of cellular processes used by some micro-organisms to extract energy from food in the absence of oxygen

13. Which of the following statements is true?

    A. The curved surface of Earth results in unequal heating of the surface, which causes wind.

    B. Wind creates thermal energy.

    C. Cool air is less dense than warm air so it sinks, creating wind.

    D. Cool air near Earth's surface rises and warms before sinking back down.

Use the diagram below to answer questions 14 to 16.

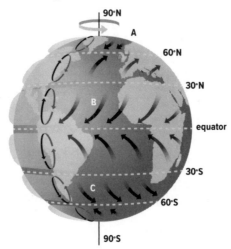

14. Which section of the globe represents the trade winds?

    A. A   **C.** C

    B. B   **D.** None of the above.

15. Which section of the globe represents the westerlies?

    A. A   **C.** C

    B. B   **D.** None of the above.

16. Which section of the globe represents the polar easterlies?

    A. A   **C.** C

    B. B   **D.** None of the above.

17. Which statement about wind is false?

    A. Wind is moving air.

    B. Wind results from an unequal heating of Earth's surface.

    C. Wind does not play an important role in redistributing thermal energy around Earth.

    D. Earth's major wind systems result from a combination of convection currents and the Coriolis effect.

18. Which set of arrows shows the flow of surface currents in an ocean basin in the northern hemisphere?

A.

C. → ←

B.

D. ← →

19. Which statement about poleward-flowing surface currents is true?

A. They carry warm, tropical water to higher, colder latitudes.

B. They carry warm, tropical water to lower, warmer latitudes.

C. They carry cold water to lower, warmer latitudes.

D. They carry cold water to higher, colder latitudes.

20. The massive system of deep-water currents produced by the sinking of surface water is the

A. California current.

C. Gulf Stream.

B. great ocean conveyor belt.

D. North Pacific Drift.

21. Complete the Venn diagram by placing the letters for each phrase below in the correct part.

A. $C_6H_{12}O_6 + O_2 \rightarrow CO_2 + H_2O$ + usable energy
B. sustains life
C. carried out by green plants and certain single-celled organisms
D. carried out by nearly all organisms on Earth
E. chemical energy is changed to other forms of energy (e.g., kinetic and thermal)
F. light energy from the Sun $+ CO_2 + H_2O \rightarrow C_6H_{12}O_6 + O_2$
G. light energy is changed to chemical energy

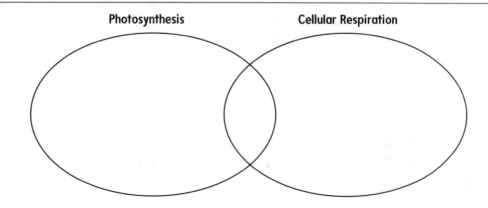

Photosynthesis   Cellular Respiration

What interactions supply energy to Earth's biosphere?

Use with textbook pages 310–317.

Food Chains

A **food chain** is a model that describes how the stored energy in food is passed on from one living thing to another. **Producers**, living things that make their own food to get the energy they need, are at the bottom of food chains. **Consumers** eat producers and other consumers to get the energy they need. The flow of energy always goes from a producer to a consumer, and on to one or more consumers in a food chain. Figure 4.12 on page 312 in the textbook shows an example of a food chain.

Food Webs

A **food web** is a model of feeding relationships that shows a network of interacting and overlapping food chains. A food web is used to show a more realistic model of feeding relationships in an ecosystem. A food web usually includes **decomposers**, which are organisms that break down dead organic material to get the energy they need. The figure below is an example of a food web.

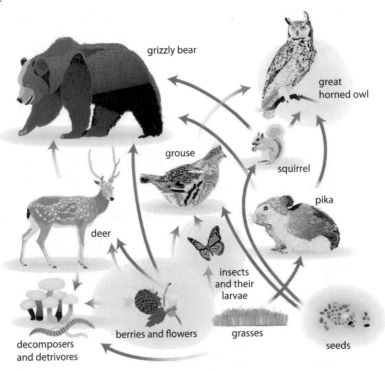

Although individual food chains can be traced within a food web, all organisms in a food web are connected to each other through their feeding relationships. If there is a change in the population of one organism, this can potentially affect several food chains or the entire food web. A food web helps show that all organisms in an ecosystem depend on each other for survival.

Energy in a Food Chain

Food chains in nature usually have between two and five levels. There are limits to the number of levels in a food chain because only about 10 percent of the food energy for a producer is available to the consumer that eats it. And only 10 percent of the food energy for that consumer is available to the next consumer. The figure below gives more information about the energy that is available at each level in a food chain.

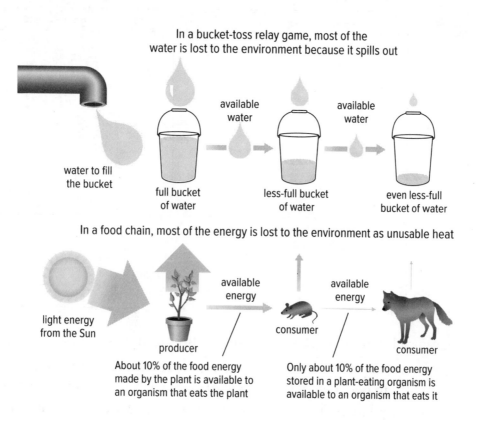

In a bucket-toss relay game, most of the water is lost to the environment because it spills out

water to fill the bucket

full bucket of water

available water

less-full bucket of water

available water

even less-full bucket of water

In a food chain, most of the energy is lost to the environment as unusable heat

light energy from the Sun

producer

About 10% of the food energy made by the plant is available to an organism that eats the plant

available energy

consumer

Only about 10% of the food energy stored in a plant-eating organism is available to an organism that eats it

available energy

consumer

What happens to all of the energy that does not move up the food chain? Some of the original food energy has been used already to support life functions, such as growth and cellular respiration. Some energy is changed into heat that is given off into the environment. Some energy is stored in wastes (urine and feces) that are excreted into the environment. Bacteria, fungi, and other decomposers extract some of this energy, but most of the energy is lost to the environment as heat. Energy lost as heat cannot be used by other living things. **An energy pyramid**, shown in Figure 4.15 on page 315 in the textbook, is a model that shows the amount of energy available in each level of a food chain.

Food Chains

Use with textbook pages 312–313.

1. Complete the table about producers, consumers, and decomposers. Note that the last column asks for an organism that is a local example.

Type of Organism	Description	Local Example
Producer		
Consumer		
Decomposer		

2. Read the paragraph below and use the information to draw a food chain in the box.

   Plankton are microscopic organisms that make their own food through photosynthesis. In an ocean ecosystem, small fish, such as herring, eat plankton. Herring are eaten by larger fish, such as cod. Sea lions eat cod. Orcas eat sea lions.

Reading a Food Web

Use with textbook page 313.

1. Interpreting Diagrams

A diagram is a simplified drawing that uses symbols to represent objects, directions, and relationships. Interpreting diagrams correctly is an important part of science literacy. Study the diagram and answer the questions below.

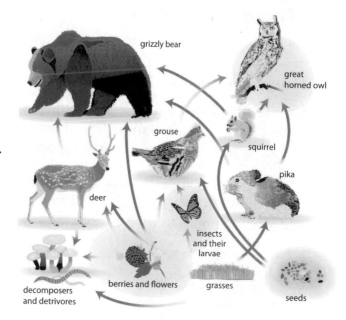

a) Which organisms are the producers?

_____

b) What does a grouse consume?

_____

c) What preys on deer?

_____

d) What preys on a great horned owl?

_____

e) What does a pika eat?

_____

f) What preys on a pika?

_____

g) How is a great horned owl connected to seeds?

_____

_____

Food Energy in a Food Chain

Use with textbook page 314.

1. Cause and Effect—Using Graphic Organizers

Identifying causes and effects can help you understand why things happen. Sometimes, multiple causes lead to an effect that itself becomes the cause of a second effect. A cause-and-effect map can help you organize such relationships.

Read the paragraphs on page 314 in the textbook. Complete the cause and effect map below showing the relationship between the limits to the length of a food chain and what happens to food energy in a food chain.

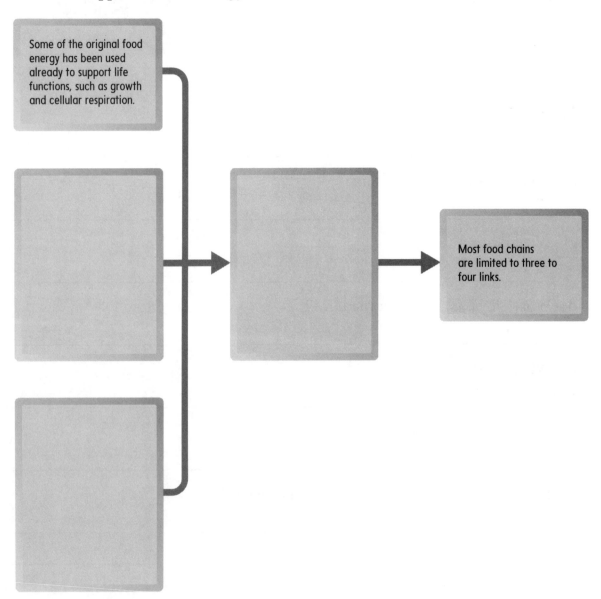

Some of the original food energy has been used already to support life functions, such as growth and cellular respiration.

Most food chains are limited to three to four links.

Energy Pyramids

Use with textbook page 315.

1. In an energy pyramid, 90% of the available energy is lost at each trophic level. Fill in the amount of energy available at each level in the energy pyramid below using the following information: Primary producers produce 5 806 000 energy units.

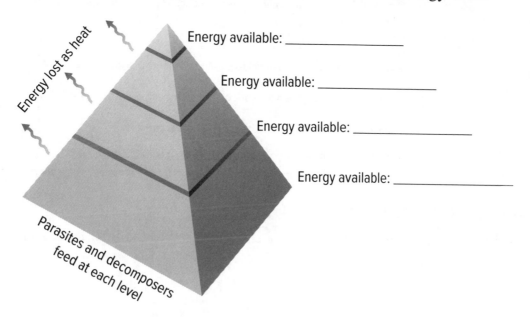

Energy lost as heat

Energy available: _____

Energy available: _____

Energy available: _____

Energy available: _____

Parasites and decomposers feed at each level

2. Write an analogy that would help another student understand what happens to the amount of energy available in each level of a food chain.

_____

_____

_____

_____

3. Write a sample problem of your own that asks someone to fill in the the amount of available energy at each level of an energy pyramid. Provide the answer as well.

_____

_____

_____

_____

4.3 Assessment

Match each description on the left with the term on the right. Each term may be used more than once.

Description	Term
1. _____ organism that makes its own food to get the energy it needs to live	A. consumer
2. _____ model that describes how the stored energy in food is passed on from one living thing to another	B. decomposer
3. _____ golden eagle that preys on a marmot	C. food chain
4. _____ organism that breaks down dead organic material to obtain the energy it needs to live	D. food web
5. _____ model of feeding relationships that shows a network of interacting and overlapping food chains	E. producer
6. _____ organism that consumes other organisms to get the energy it needs to live	
7. _____ grasses that carry out photosynthesis	

Circle the letter of the best answer for questions 8 to 17.

8. In a food chain, each time energy is transferred to the next level some of the energy is lost as unusable

    A. heat.   **C.** waste.

    B. food.   **D.** water.

9. Which is **not** a reason why only a small percent of food energy is available at the next level of an energy pyramid?

    A. Some of the original food energy has been used already to support life functions, such as growth and cellular respiration.

    B. Some energy is changed into heat that is given off into the environment. This energy cannot be used by other living things.

    C. Some energy is stored in wastes (urine and feces) that are excreted into the environment.

    D. There is a constant flow of energy needed to sustain living things in terrestrial and aquatic ecosystems.

10. In an energy pyramid, how much energy is lost with each step up?

    A. 10%   **C.** 50%

    B. 25%   **D.** 90%

11. If the algae in the food chain shown produce 10 000 energy units, how many energy units are available for the small fish?

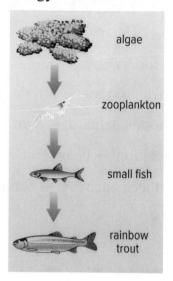

A. 10

B. 100

C. 1 000

D. 10 000

Use the diagram of the food web to answer questions 12 to 17.

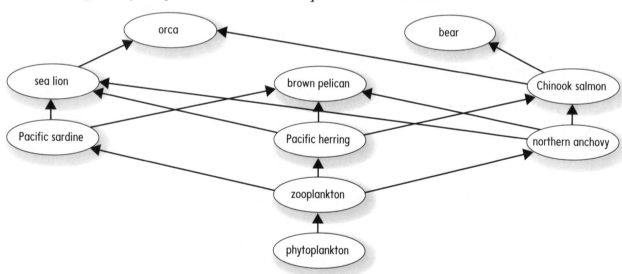

12. Which organisms are preyed on by brown pelicans?

A. orcas, zooplankton, Pacific herring

B. Pacific sardine, Chinook salmon, bear

C. northern anchovy, Pacific herring, Pacific sardine

D. sea lion, phytoplankton, northern anchovy

13. Which of the following organisms has no predators in this food web?

    A. Chinook salmon   **C.** Pacific herring

    B. orca   **D.** sea lion

14. Which represents a food chain within the food web?

    A. phytoplankton → zooplankton → Pacific herring → brown pelican

    B. zooplankton → Pacific herring → Chinook salmon → bear

    C. phytoplankton → Pacific sardine → sea lion → bear

    D. zooplankton → Pacific herring → northern anchovy → sea lion

15. Which organisms consume zooplankton?

    A. sea lion, brown pelican, northern anchovy

    B. phytoplankton, Chinook salmon, orca

    C. Pacific sardine, Pacific herring, northern anchovy

    D. bear, orca, sea lion

16. Which organisms are the producers in this food web?

    A. brown pelican   **C.** phytoplankton

    B. northern anchovy   **D.** zooplankton

17. What are the most levels of any food chain in this food web?

    A. 3   **C.** 5

    B. 4   **D.** 6

18. Complete the Venn diagram to show the similarities and differences between a food chain and a food web.

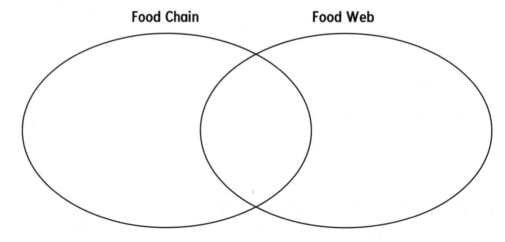

Food Chain   Food Web

What interactions cycle matter through Earth's spheres?

Use with textbook pages 320–335.

The Water Cycle

The water cycle is driven by solar energy and gravity. Important processes in the water cycle include evaporation, condensation, precipitation, and transpiration.

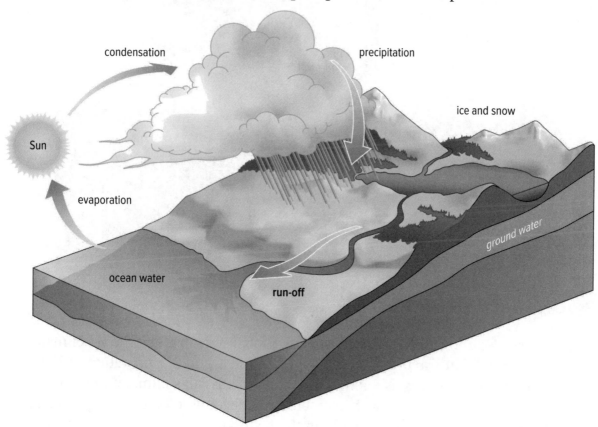

Transpiration is the process by which water is absorbed by the roots of plants, carried through the plant, and lost as water vapour through small pores in the leaves. Refer to Figure 4.17 on page 323 in the textbook to see how transpiration works.

Water pollution is any physical, biological, or chemical change in water quality that has an adverse effect on organisms or that makes water unsuitable for desired uses. Water pollution can be traced back to point sources, but many times it comes from non-point sources. Some types of pollutants, such as DDT, mercury, and PCBs, can accumulate and become concentrated in the tissues of aquatic organisms.

Bioaccumulation is the process by which pollutants collect in the cells and tissues of organisms. **Biomagnification** is an increase in the concentration of pollutants in the tissues of organisms that are at successively higher levels in a food chain or food web. Figure 4.19 on page 325 in the textbook shows an example of bioaccumulation and biomagnification.

Nutrients Are Cycled Through Interactions Between Living and Non-living Things

The figure below shows how carbon is cycled through all of Earth's spheres.

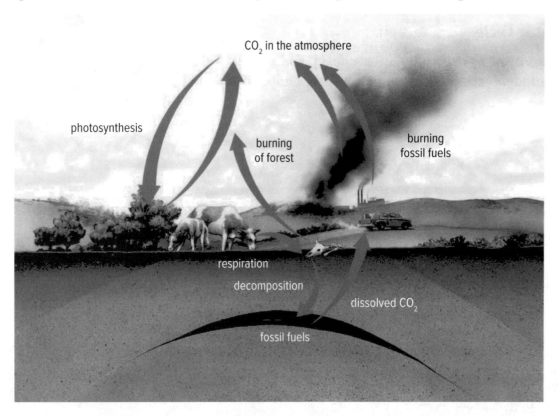

When an excess of carbon enters the atmosphere, global warming and global climate change can occur. **Global warming** is an increase in the average temperature of Earth's surface. **Global climate change** is a long-term change in Earth's climate. In the last 100 years Earth's surface temperature has been increasing, leading to other changes such as the ones shown in Figure 4.22 on page 328 in the textbook.

Nitrogen is a major part of all cells and a key building block for proteins. Although 78% of the atmosphere is made up of nitrogen, bacteria in soil and water must change nitrogen in the air into forms that can be used by living things. Figure 4.24 on page 330 in the textbook shows how nitrogen moves through the atmosphere, biosphere, hydrosphere, and geosphere. When excess nitrogen enters the hydrosphere, it can cause algal blooms, as shown in Figure 4.25 on page 331 in the textbook.

Phosphorus has a short-term cycle in which it cycles through living things and the hydrosphere and geosphere. The long-term cycle of phosphorus involves phosphorus being washed from land into the ocean and then stored in limestone and sandstone. Refer to Figure 4.26 on page 332 in the textbook to see how phosphorus moves through Earth's spheres. Like nitrogen, if an excess of phosphorus enters the hydrosphere, an algal bloom can result.

The Water Cycle

Use with textbook pages 322–325.

1. Illustrate the water cycle in the space below. Be sure to include labels for the following processes: condensation, evaporation, precipitation, run-off, and transpiration.

2. Explain how, through the water cycle, the hydrosphere interacts with Earth's other spheres.

_____

_____

_____

_____

3. Using the terms *bioaccumulation* and *biomagnification*, explain how humans can impact the water cycle.

_____

_____

_____

_____

Climate Change

Use with textbook page 327.

1. Interpreting Line Graphs

Line graphs show relationships between two variables. To interpret a line graph, start by reading the title of the graph, the labels on the *x*-axis and *y*-axis, and the caption. Then, look for patterns or trends in the shape of the graph.

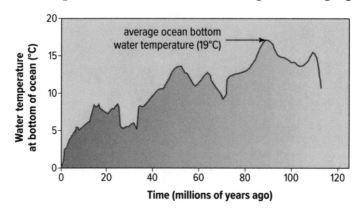

a) Does the graph have a title? If not, write a title for the graph.

_____

b) What is the label on the *x*-axis? What is the label on the *y*-axis?

_____

_____

c) The caption for this graph states "High levels of volcanic activity released greenhouse gases that warmed global temperatures significantly during the late Cretaceous period. As a result, scientists estimate that the temperature of water at the bottom of the ocean was near 19 °C." Explain the caption in your own words.

_____

_____

d) Describe the relationship between the two variables.

_____

_____

2. Use the trend in the graph to make a prediction about the future if global temperatures increase significantly.

_____

Effects of Excess Carbon

Use with textbook pages 328–329.

Evaluate each effect of excess carbon in the carbon cycle. For each effect, predict a social, economic, and ecological impact.

1. Land and sea ice melts, which leads to rising sea level.

   a) Social impact:

   _____

   b) Economic impact:

   _____

   c) Ecological impact:

   _____

2. Warmer seawater absorbs more CO_2, making seawater more acidic.

   a) Social impact:

   _____

   b) Economic impact:

   _____

   c) Ecological impact:

   _____

3. Extreme weather events increase, leading to more frequent heat waves and severe storms.

   a) Social impact:

   _____

   b) Economic impact:

   _____

   c) Ecological impact:

   _____

Algal Blooms

Use with textbook page 331.

1. Flowcharts—Using Graphic Organizers

A flowchart shows a sequence of events or steps in a process. A flowchart starts with the first event or step. An arrow leads to the next event or step and continues until the final outcome. All of the events or steps are shown in the order in which they occur.

Complete the flowchart below to sequence the steps involved in the formation, progression, and final effects of an algal bloom in an aquatic ecosystem. Use Figure 4.25 of page 331 of the textbook to help you.

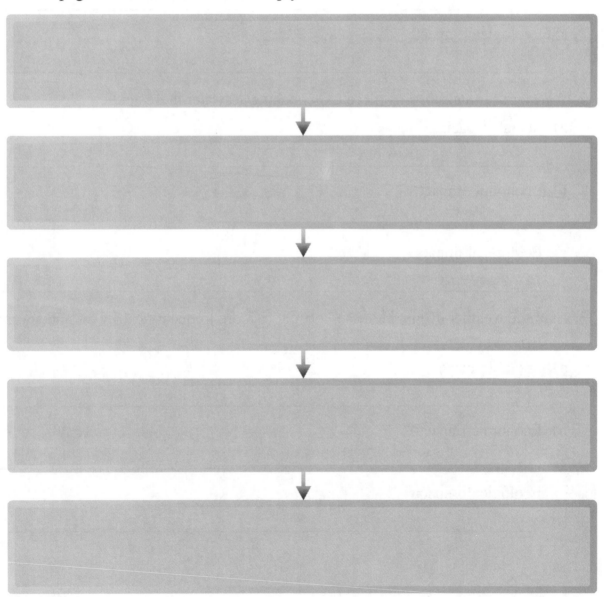

The Phosphorus Cycle

Use with textbook pages 332–333.

Use the diagram of the phosphorus cycle to answer the questions.

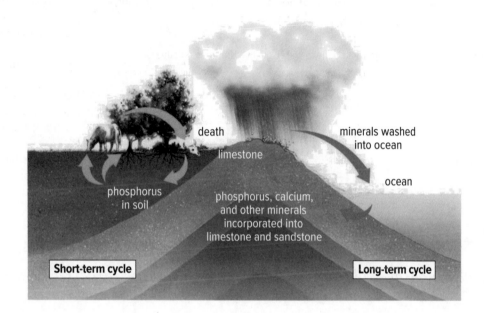

1. How does the phosphorus cycle show interactions among the geosphere, the hydrosphere, and the biosphere?

_____

_____

_____

_____

_____

_____

2. What role does the atmosphere play in the phosphorus cycle?

_____

_____

3. What is the difference between the short-term phosphorus cycle and the long-term phosphorus cycle?

_____

_____

4.4 Assessment

Match each definition on the left with a term on the right. Each term may be used only once.

Description	Term
1. ____ process by which water is absorbed by roots of plants, carried through the plant, and lost as water vapour through small pores in the leaves	A. bioaccumulation
2. ____ any physical, biological, or chemical change in water quality that has an adverse effect on organisms or that makes unsuitable for desired uses	B. biomagnification
3. ____ process by which pollutants collect in the cells and tissues of organisms	C. global climate change
4. ____ the increase in concentration of pollutants in tissues of organisms that are at successively higher levels in a food chain or food web	D. global warming
5. ____ an increase in the average temperature of Earth's surface	E. transpiration
6. ____ a long-term change in Earth's climate	F. water pollution

Mark each statement as true (T) or false (F). If a statement is false, correct it so that it is true.

7. _____ Gravity and solar energy drive the water cycle.

_____

8. _____ About 50% of water vapour in the atmosphere is released by plants.

_____

9. _____ Examples of water pollutants include DDT, mercury, and PCBs.

_____

10. _____ Carbon enters the atmosphere when the remains of organisms become deeply buried in the ground.

_____

11. _____ In the past 100 years, Earth's surface temperature has decreased.

_____

12. _____ Nitrogen is a major part of all cells and a key building block for proteins.

_____

13. _____ In the short term, phosphorus is stored in the geosphere.

_____

Circle the letter of the best answer for questions 14 to 21.

14. Plants in water absorb phosphorus. Animals obtain phosphorus when they eat other organisms. These are examples of phosphorus interacting with which of Earth's spheres?

   A. atmosphere   **C.** geosphere

   B. biosphere   **D.** hydrosphere

15. Excess nitrogen and phosphorus in run-off contributes to

   A. algal blooms.   **C.** smart growth.

   B. global warming.   **D.** transpiration.

16. Nitrogen makes up 78% of air, but most living things cannot use nitrogen from the air. Nitrogen-fixing bacteria in soil and water change nitrogen into forms that plants can use. Which of Earth's spheres are interacting in this example?

   A. atmosphere and biosphere

   B. biosphere and geosphere

   C. atmosphere, geosphere, and hydrosphere

   D. hydrosphere, geosphere, biosphere, and atmosphere

17. Which processes are important parts of the carbon cycle?

   A. bioaccumulation and biomagnification

   B. photosynthesis and cellular respiration

   C. recycling and smart growth

   D. transpiration and decomposition

18. In which cycle do the processes of evaporation, condensation, and precipitation play important roles?

   A. carbon cycle   **C.** phosphorus cycle

   B. nitrogen cycle   **D.** water cycle

19. Which of the following is an example of a non-point source of water pollution?

   A. factories

   B. oil wells

   C. run-off from roads and parking lots

   D. sewage treatment plants

20. Within a food chain, zooplankton have a concentration of 0.05 ppm of DDT in their tissues. Within that same food chain, fish-eating birds have a concentration of 25 ppm in their tissues. This is an example of which of the following?

   A. bioaccumulation   **C.** greenhouse effect

   B. biomagnification   **D.** transpiration

21. Which of the following is a consequence of melting land and sea ice due to global warming?

   A. Increased cases of heat-related illness in humans.

   B. Increased acidity dissolves the calcium in coral.

   C. Seawater absorbing more carbon dioxide from the air.

   D. Salt water intruding into underground supplies of drinking water.

22. Complete the table below to show the similarities and differences among the different nutrient cycles.

Question	Carbon Cycle	Nitrogen Cycle	Phosphorus Cycle
What is cycled?			
How is the hydrosphere involved?			
How is the atmosphere involved?			
How is the biosphere involved?			
How is the geosphere involved?			
What happens if excess nutrients enter the cycle?			

How can our actions promote sustainability?

Use with textbook pages 340–347.

Individuals Can Make a Difference

Table 4.5 on page 342 in the textbook lists the different ways individuals can be empowered to promote sustainability. For example,

- consumers have power in deciding what products they will buy and not buy.
- citizens can volunteer.
- citizens have responsibility to their communities, province, and the planet.
- citizen scientists contribute to the information scientists use to learn more about sustainability.
- a citizen may join a science-minded advocacy group to help protect ecosystems and ecosystem services.

Responsible Decision Making Is Important to Promote Sustainability

There are many ways that individuals, advocacy groups, businesses, and cities can help promote sustainability. Figure 4.28 on page 344 in the textbook gives some examples. One example is **smart growth**, a strategy that focuses on concentrating growth in the centre of a city, rather than in outlying areas. Smart growth helps combat urban sprawl. When cities expand with smart growth, green spaces are preserved and public transport is usually improved.

There are several things that can be done to help reduce the amount of greenhouse gases released into the atmosphere. Businesses can install solar panels, which reduces the amount of electricity generated from burning fossil fuels. Some cities, such as Vancouver, are promoting bicycle-sharing programs as well as making the roadways safer for bicyclers. Riding bicycles instead of using automobiles reduces the amount of fossil fuels burned. Building sustainably, including using geothermal heating to heat homes, can also reduce fossil fuel use.

Recycling programs in schools, businesses, and cities help reduce the amount of waste produced. Reducing, reusing, recycling, and composting can all cut back on the amount of wastes reaching landfills. Building sustainably also reduces waste because some materials are repurposed, such as using trees that are removed as part of construction to make fireplace mantels in the homes.

Designating an area as a Dark Sky Preserve helps reduce the effects of artificial lighting on the nighttime environment. This helps protect the wildlife that use the area as their habitat. Animals that are nocturnal are negatively affected by light pollution.

Examples of Individual Empowerment

Use with textbook page 342.

1. Interpreting Tables

A table is made up of cells that are organized into rows and columns. Each cell contains information or data. Each column and row has a heading to help you interpret each cell.

a) The title of Table 4.5 on page 342 in the textbook is *Examples of Individual Empowerment*. Based on the title, explain what kind of information you expect to see in the cells.

_____

_____

_____

b) Refer to Table 4.5 on page 342 in the textbook. Read the column and row headings. Explain what they mean.

_____

_____

_____

c) Pick any three cells in the table. Record which cell it is by stating the column and row it appears in. For example, column 1, row 1 shows a woman reading the label on a box of cereal. Write a summary of the content in each cell using your own words.

Cell: column _____, row _____

_____

_____

Cell: column _____, row _____

_____

_____

Cell: column _____, row _____

_____

_____

Sustainable Practices

Use with textbook pages 344–345.

1. Complete the table below to show the results of actions taken to promote sustainability. One example is filled in for you.

Action	Results
Building sustainable housing	
Designating Dark Sky Preserves	
Expanding a city through smart growth	
Installing solar panels	
Promoting bicycling	
Recycling	reduces waste; materials may be recycled, reused, or composted; waste reduction plans can be enacted

Promoting Sustainability

Use with textbook pages 344–345.

1. Choose one example of something you are doing or have done to promote sustainability. Write two or three paragraphs and use the 5 Ws (who, what, where, when, and why) to help you structure your response.

_____

_____

_____

_____

_____

_____

_____

_____

_____

_____

_____

_____

_____

_____

_____

_____

_____

_____

_____

_____

_____

_____

_____

_____

_____

4.5 Assessment

Match each example of individual empowerment on the left with the type of empowerment on the right. Each type of empowerment may be used more than once.

Description	Type of Empowerment
1. ____ A person reads a food label and decides not to buy the product because it is not B.C. Certified Organic.	A. Citizens have responsibility.
2. ____ A person participates in the Audubon Christmas Bird Count, a survey in which people spend a day identifying and counting birds in a specific area. Audubon compiles the data annually, and the data are used by scientists to monitor changes in bird populations.	B. Citizen scientists can make important contributions to science.
3. ____ A person joins Ducks Unlimited Canada, an organization that works to conserve wetlands and other ecosystems and the organisms that inhabit them.	C. Consumers have power.
4. ____ A person makes sure to purchase a refrigerator that has an ENERGY STAR® rating.	D. Science-minded advocacy groups can effect change, and increase sustainability and stewardship.
5. ____ A person volunteers to answer questions about food labels at a local farmers' market.	E. Volunteers inspire through their commitment and example.
6. ____ A person reads articles and blogs from several different sources about a candidate before they vote.	
7. ____ A person researches a local environmental group to find out more about what they represent and how they carry out their mission statement.	

Circle the letter of the best answer for questions 8 to 15.

8. Which question represents an example of a citizen having responsibility?

A. How can a person educate themselves about candidates before they vote?

B. Who benefits from a person's willingness to share part of themselves?

C. How can a person find out more about the manufacturing conditions and materials used to make a product?

D. How can the work a person does as a member of an advocacy group lead to changes in legislation that help protect ecosystems and ecosystem services?

9. Which term describes the strategy that focuses on concentrating growth in the centre of a city, rather than outlying areas?

A. recycling

C. sustainable building

B. smart growth

D. urban sprawl

10. Which question represents the idea that consumers have power?

    A. In what ways are you a citizen of your community? your province? your country?

    B. What local projects interest you?

    C. What choices do you make about the products you will and will not buy?

    D. How can you find out more information about local projects you could participate in, such as a wildflower survey?

11. Which term describes what happens as cities with growing populations increase their size by spreading into natural areas and farmland?

    A. recycling

    B. smart growth

    C. sustainable building

    D. urban sprawl

12. Which question represents an example that citizen scientists can make important contributions to science?

    A. How can volunteering locally have global effects?

    B. How can your local data be used nationally or internationally to help scientists learn more about sustainability?

    C. How can you find out more about advocacy groups and their motives, backing, and the cause they represent?

    D. What reasons lie behind or motivate your choices?

13. Which question represents the idea that volunteers inspire others through their commitment and example?

    A. How can volunteering locally have global effects?

    B. What responsibilities do you have as a citizen?

    C. How can your local data be used nationally or internationally to help scientists learn more about sustainability?

    D. How can a person find out more about the manufacturing conditions and materials used to make a product?

14. Which question represents the idea that science-minded advocacy groups can effect change, and increase sustainability and stewardship?

   A. How can a person educate themselves about candidates before they vote?

   B. Who benefits from a person's willingness to share part of themselves?

   C. How can a person find out more about the manufacturing conditions and materials used to make a product?

   D. How can the work a person does as a member of an advocacy group lead to changes in legislation that help protect ecosystems and ecosystem services?

15. What does the photo represent?

   A. biomagnification

   B. interconnectedness

   C. smart growth

   D. urban sprawl

16. Use the phrases in the box below to fill in the concept map.

bicycle-sharing program	installing solar panels
designating a Dark Sky Preserve	recycling
building sustainable housing	

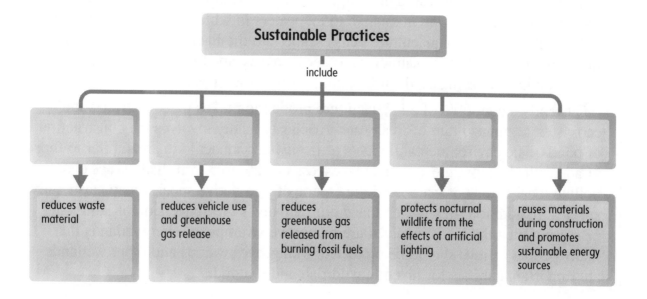

How can aquaculture affect the sustainability of natural ecosystems?

What's the Issue?

Aquaculture is the breeding, raising, and harvesting of animals in specially designed aquatic environments. Aquaculture is commonly called fish farming. In many aquaculture operations, fish and seafood are raised in pens that are either close to shore in marine environments, or in deeper water farther offshore. Raising fish in concentrated settings can affect the sustainability of the natural ecosystems in which they are located. For example, increased nutrients, such as nitrogen, are released into the surrounding water from uneaten food and the wastes produced by the fish. This can cause local algal blooms that affect the surrounding natural ecosystem. Shellfish, such as clams and oysters, are especially vulnerable when oxygen levels in the water drop. Net pens anchored near shore allow the spread of disease, antibiotics, and other pollutants into surrounding ecosystems.

One example of a problem associated with salmon farming is sea lice. These are parasites that infect both farmed and wild salmon. Scientists estimate that in the early 2000s, sea lice associated with salmon farms near Vancouver Island accounted for 90% of the deaths of juvenile wild salmon after deaths from other known causes were counted. A new approach to treating farmed salmon for sea lice has reduced the impact of sea lice on wild populations in the area. There are still concerns, though, that the sea lice are becoming resistant to the parasite treatments.

Another way that near-shore aquaculture operations may affect the sustainability of natural ecosystems is through escaped fish. For example, many of the salmon species raised in farms are not native to the waters in which they are raised. When Atlantic salmon from aquaculture pens escape into the Pacific Ocean, they compete for food with wild Pacific salmon. In other areas, escaped fish may compete with wild individuals for mates, disturb habitat, or become invasive.

Currently, about 60% of all aquaculture production takes place in freshwater ecosystems. Aquaculture of freshwater species typically involves the construction of ponds. The environmental impacts of freshwater aquaculture are similar to those of aquaculture in marine systems. An excess of nutrients from fish wastes can pollute local bodies of water, and the escape of non-native species may harm native species. In addition, freshwater aquaculture involves the conversion of land to a new use. Often the lands involved are mangrove swamps or other wetlands that many people believe should be protected. Mangrove swamps and other wetlands are important habitats for juvenile wild fish and seafood.

Dig Deeper

Collaborate with your classmates to explore one or more of these questions—or generate your own questions to explore.

1. Research aquaculture operations in British Columbia. What types of fish and/or seafood are farmed there? in what quantities?

2. Find out more about how aquaculture systems can affect the nitrogen and phosphorus cycles. How can the impact of aquaculture on nutrient cycles affect the sustainability of nearby natural ecosystems?

3. Research the current issues of sea lice in salmon aquaculture in British Columbia. What are some alternative approaches to raising salmon to help reduce or avoid sea lice infections? How could the alternative approaches affect the sustainability of natural ecosystems in both positive and negative ways?

4. Research some ways that fish in aquaculture pens escape into natural ecosystems. How can escaped fish affect the sustainability of natural ecosystems?

5. Find out more about how the construction of aquaculture operations affects the sustainability of wetlands, such as mangrove forests.

6. Use what you have learned from your research to make suggestions for how aquaculture operations can be run more sustainably.

Notes:

Notes: